What is a DINGBAT?

It's a cunningly disguised name or saying that's turned around, upside-down, sideways or all jumbled up!

And here they are! One mind-boggling collection that will drive you crazy!

Also published by Corgi Books:

DEMON DINGBATS®
DASTARDLY DINGBATS®
DIABOLICAL DINGBATS®
DEVILISH DINGBATS®

Junior DINGBATS Challenge

Junior DINGBATS® Challenge

The book that will drive you crazy!

YOUNG CORGI

JUNIOR DINGBATS® CHALLENGE

A CORGI BOOK 0 552 525375

Originally published in Great Britain by Corgi Books

PRINTING HISTORY
Corgi edition published 1988

This book is set in Optima.

Corgi Books are published by Transworld Publishers Ltd., 61-63 Uxbridge Road, Ealing, London W5 5SA, in Australia by Transworld Publishers (Australia) Pty. Ltd., 15-23 Helles Avenue, Moorebank, NSW 2170, and in New Zealand by Transworld Publishers (N.Z.) Ltd., Cnr. Moselle and Waipareira Avenues, Henderson, Auckland.

Made and printed in Great Britain by
The Guernsey Press Co. Ltd., Guernsey, Channel Islands

INTRODUCTION

Welcome to the Junior DINGBATS Challenge!

The original DINGBATS board game was a runaway success when it was launched by Waddingtons in 1987 and rapidly became one of the four best-selling games. Voted the *Toy Trader* Best Toy of the Year and winner of the *What Toy* Best Family Game Award, it plays delightful games with common words and phrases, forcing players to think in new ways. Mind-boggling, frustrating and incredibly fascinating, the game appeals to players of all ages and has sold millions of copies all round the world.

Now there is a Junior DINGBATS game, specially created for younger players (though many adults like to play this game too). The Junior DINGBATS Challenge Book is for anyone who likes to be driven completely crazy by these zany phrase and word puzzles. It can be used by one person, or can be used as a challenge game between two players. The book is divided into different sections of graded difficulty and gets a lot harder as you go through it. Eventually, you reach the Diabolical Dingbats, which are the hardest of all. Good luck!

This book will drive you crazy!

WHAT IS A DINGBAT?

A Dingbat is a cunningly disguised name, phrase or saying, which is turned around, upside-down, on its side or all jumbled up. All you have to do is to guess the hidden word of phrase. Sounds easy? Well, sometimes it is and sometimes it isn't. Here are some examples to help you understand:

Sometimes the SIZE of the letters in the box is important.

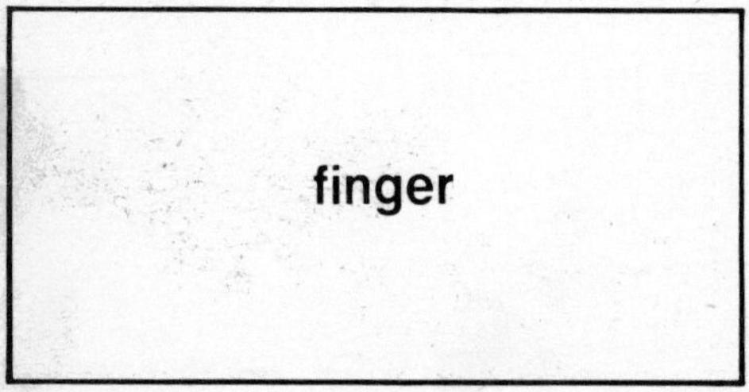

Or the POSITION of the word in relation to the box can give you the clue.

Sometimes you have to read the word in a strange DIRECTION and this is bound to be a clue. Here you have to read the word UPwards.

N
W
O
R
G

Occasionally there will be a PICTURE in the box as well as a word and when you put the two together you have your answer.

Some of the hardest Dingbats involve a clever PLAY ON WORDS. Here you have the word 'sock' printed twice. Two socks = a pair of socks. Sometimes the play on words can include NUMBERS as well. Watch out for these!

SOCK SOCK

Near the end of the book you will also find a section which uses COLOUR as part of the clue. The colour is always important and part of the answer.

HOW TO PLAY THE DINGBAT CHALLENGE

You can use this book in two ways, either by playing the solo game, or by challenging a friend to a duel. With over one hundred Dingbats in the book, there are plenty of opportunitites to play both ways.

The Solo Game

All you have to do is to see how many Dingbats in each section you can solve correctly. Fill in as many as you can and then turn to the last page of the section to check your answers and award the appropriate marks. The early sections award one point for each correct answer, the later sections award more. See how high a score you can get!

If you want to use this book again, write your answers lightly in pencil in the boxes and rub them out afterwards.

The Duel

To be played with two players. You each take it in turn to attempt to answer three Dingbats from the section of your choice. You can choose the section but your opponent chooses the number of the Dingbat you have to answer. As before, the early sections award one point for a correct answer and the later sections award more. If you answer three Dingbats correctly in one turn, you are awarded a bonus point and the turn passes to your opponent. The first player to get to 50 points wins.

MIX & MATCH DINGBATS

Just to get you started, here are six Dingbats with their answers jumbled up. See if you can match the Dingbats to their answers correctly.

BLACKSMITH

CROSS ROADS

BACK DOOR

WeLLINGTON

SET UP

FALL OVER

T
E
S

WELLINGTON BOOTS

Smith

EASY DINGBATS

*****

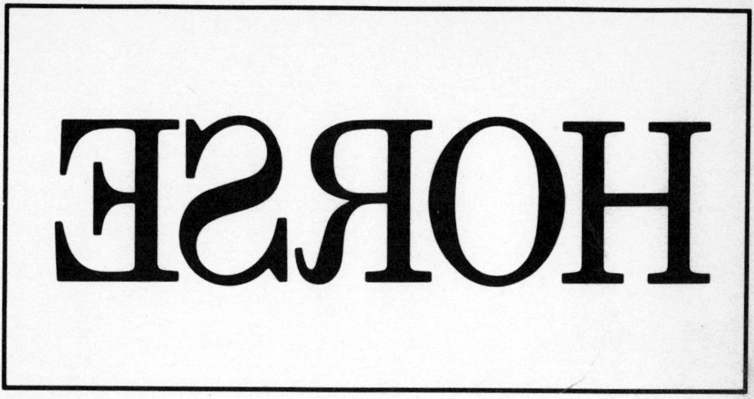

1

2

* EASY DINGBATS®

Pig Pig Pig

3

E
K
A
W

4

LEAF
LEAF
LEAF
LEAF

CLOVER

(5)

STAND

———

I

(6)

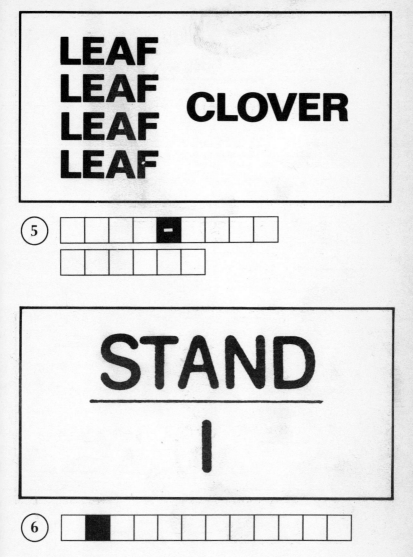

* EASY DINGBATS®

7

8

dance

(9)

scissor
scissor

(10)

* EASY DINGBATS®

BAD

WOLF

(11)

TOP TOP
TOP TOP
TOP TOP
TOP TOP
TOP TOP

(12)

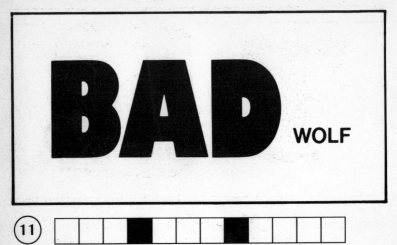

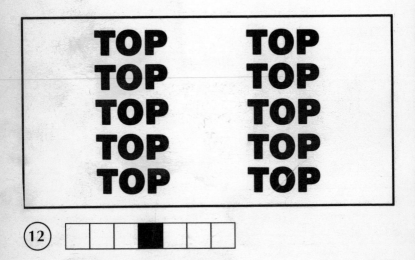

13

14

EASY DINGBATS: ANSWERS

One point

	SOLO	DUAL
1. Horseback	☐	☐
2. Broken heart	☐	☐
3. Three Little Pigs	☐	☐
4. Wake up	☐	☐
5. Four-leaf clover	☐	☐
6. I understand	☐	☐
7. Tired out	☐	☐
8. Headquarters	☐	☐
9. Tap dance	☐	☐
10. Pair of scissors	☐	☐
11. Big bad Wolf	☐	☐
12. Top Ten	☐	☐
13. Tea bag	☐	☐
14. Skipping rope	☐	☐
BONUS	☐	☐

NOT-SO-EASY DINGBATS

*****

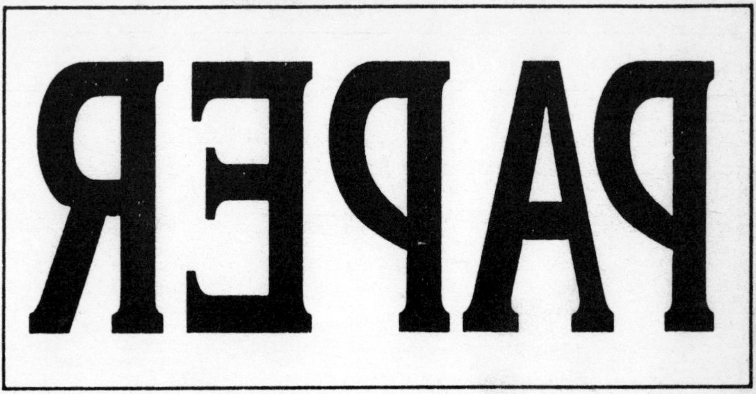

(1)

(2)

* NOT-SO-EASY DINGBATS®

(3)

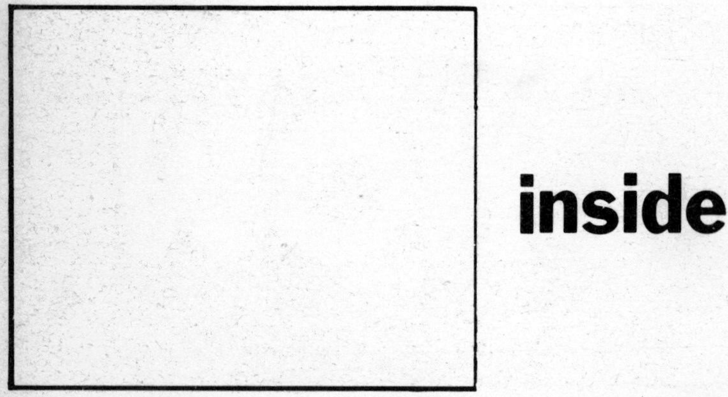

(4)

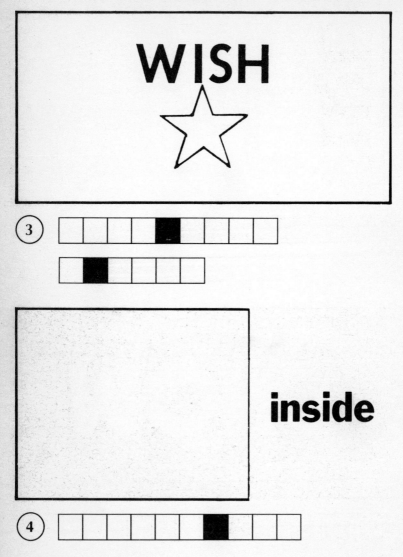

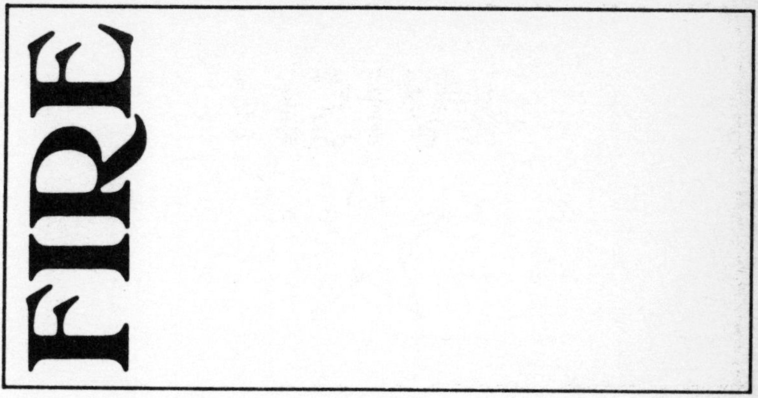

5

6

* NOT-SO-EASY DINGBATS®

7

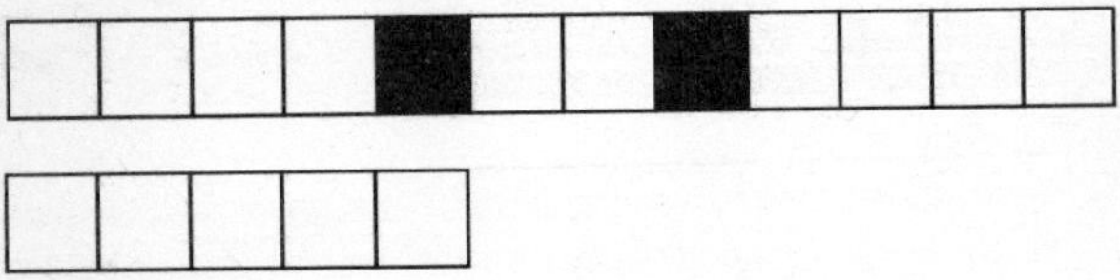

8

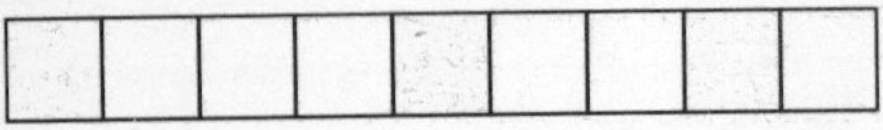

late school
school
school
school

9

TIME T
E
TIME G

10

* NOT-SO-EASY DINGBATS®

(11)

(12)

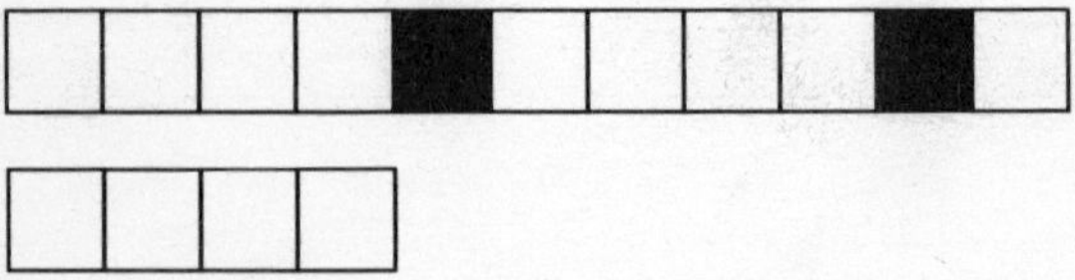

R
E
N
N
U
R

13

JUMP

14

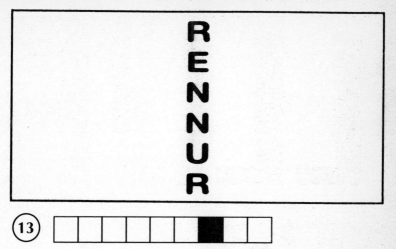

NOT-SO-EASY DINGBATS: ANSWERS

One point

	SOLO	DUAL
1. Paperback	☐	☐
2. Giant	☐	☐
3. Wish upon a star	☐	☐
4. Inside out	☐	☐
5. Fireside	☐	☐
6. Snow White	☐	☐
7. Ants in your pants	☐	☐
8. Milkshake	☐	☐
9. Late for school	☐	☐
10. Time to get up	☐	☐
11. Full back	☐	☐
12. Once upon a time	☐	☐
13. Runner-up	☐	☐
14. High jump	☐	☐
BONUS	☐	☐

TRICKY DINGBATS

*****

CLOUD CLOUD CLOUD
CLOUD **HEAD** CLOUD
CLOUD CLOUD CLOUD

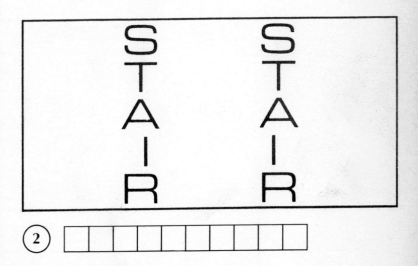

(1)

S S
T T
A A
I I
R R

(2)

* TRICKY DINGBATS®

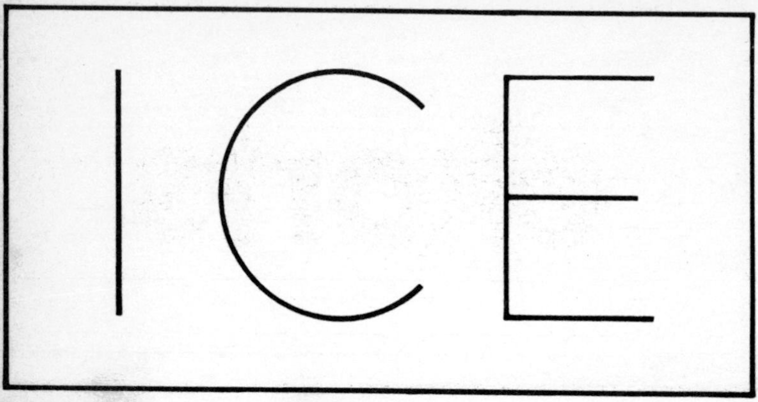

(3)

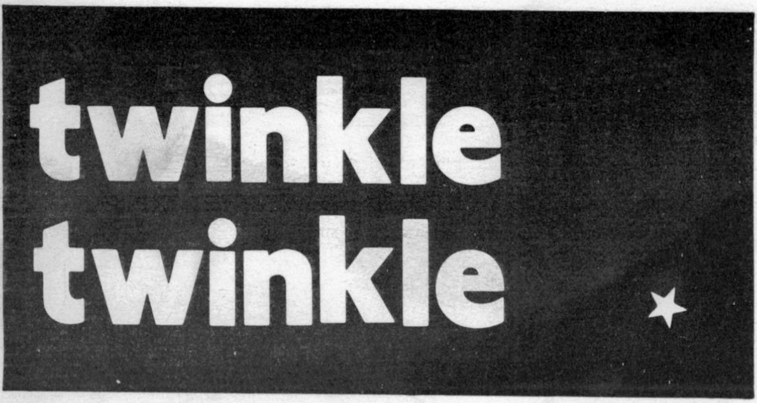

(4)

ekorts

(5) | | | | | | | | | | |

coast _

(6) | | | | | | | | | |

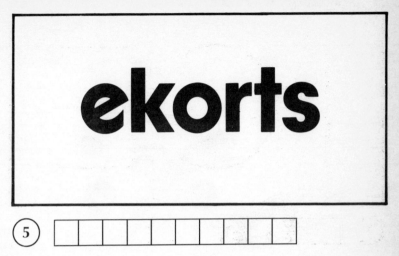

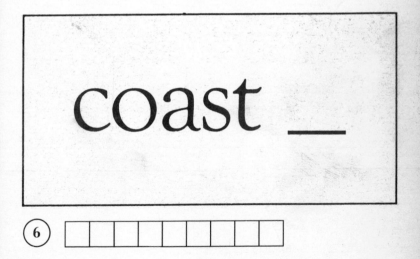

ever
ever
ever
ever

ever

7

miss muffet

8

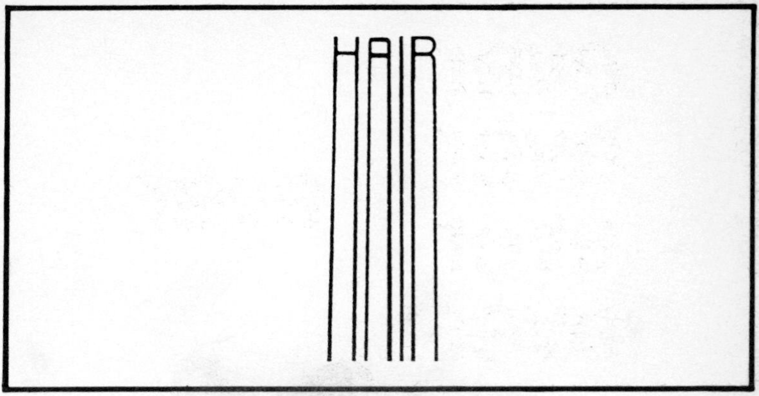

9

10

LOCK KEY

(11)

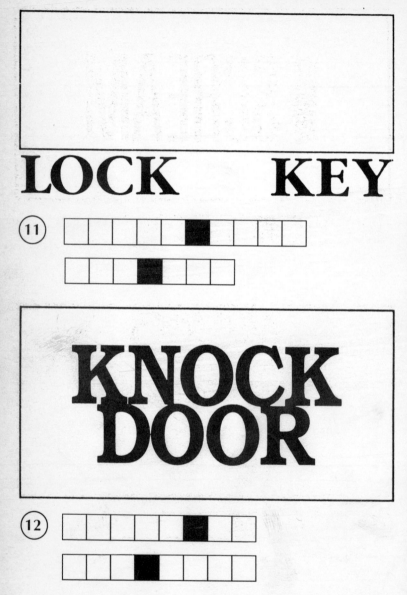

KNOCK
DOOR

(12)

iSCREAM

(13)

MARKS

(14)

TRICKY DINGBATS: ANSWERS

Two points

	SOLO	DUAL
1. Head in the clouds	☐	☐
2. Downstairs	☐	☐
3. Thin ice	☐	☐
4. Twinkle, twinkle, little star	☐	☐
5. Backstroke	☐	☐
6. Coastline	☐	☐
7. Forever and ever	☐	☐
8. Little Miss Muffet	☐	☐
9. Long hair	☐	☐
10. Lazybones	☐	☐
11. Under lock and key	☐	☐
12. Knock on the door	☐	☐
13. Ice-cream	☐	☐
14. High marks	☐	☐
BONUS	☐	☐

DIFFICULT DINGBATS

*****

WINK	WINK	WINK	WINK	WINK
WINK	WINK	WINK	WINK	WINK
WINK	WINK	WINK	WINK	WINK
WINK	WINK	WINK	WINK	WINK
WINK	WINK	WINK	WINK	WINK
WINK	WINK	WINK	WINK	WINK
WINK	WINK	WINK	WINK	WINK
WINK	WINK	WINK	WINK	WINK

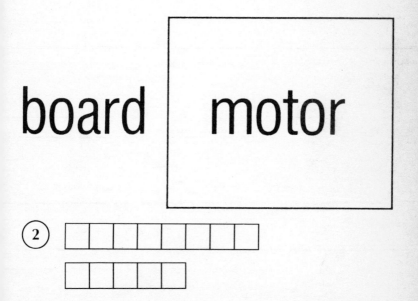

(1)

board

motor

(2)

* DIFFICULT DINGBATS®

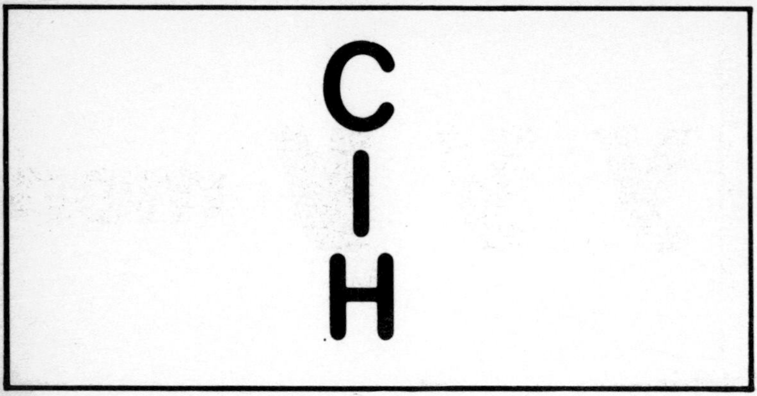

(3) ☐☐☐☐☐☐

(4) ☐☐☐☐☐☐☐☐

y y y men

(5)

(6)

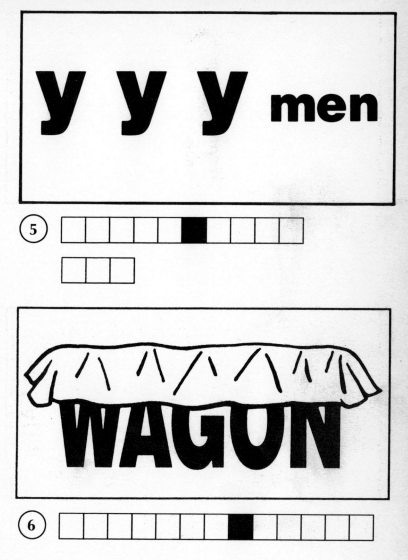

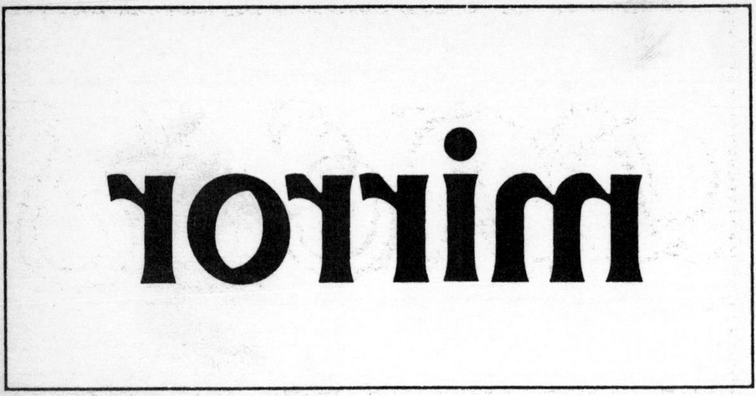

(7)

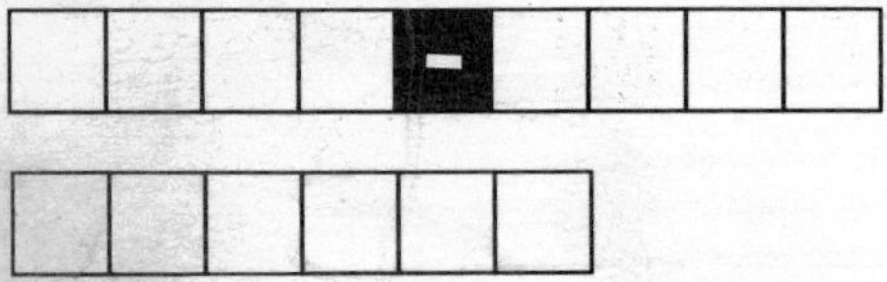

(8)

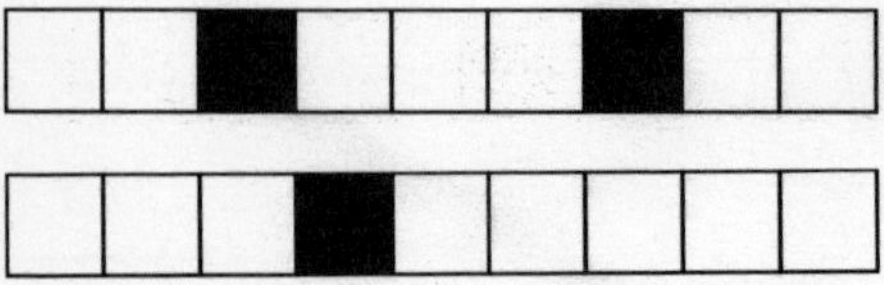

DRESS

9

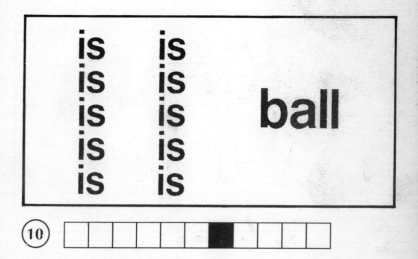

is is
is is
is is ball
is is
is is

10

* DIFFICULT DINGBATS®

VOLTAGE

(11)

P
M
U
J

A
N
D

(12)

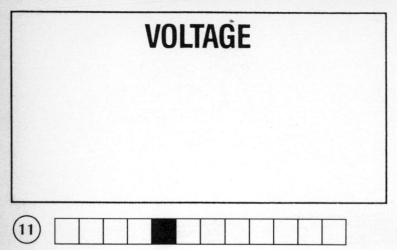

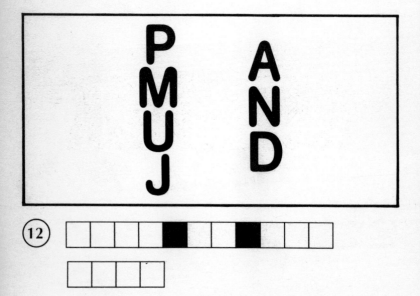

LILY
ROSEPANSY
CHRYSANTHEMUM
DAISYPOPPY
DAFFODIL
TULIP

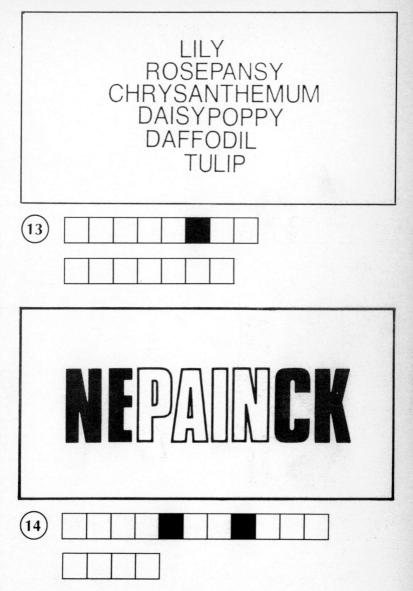

(13)

NEPAINCK

(14)

DIFFICULT DINGBATS:ANSWERS

Two points

	SOLO	DUAL
1. Forty winks		
2. Outboard motor		
3. Hiccup		
4. Earrings		
5. Three Wise Men		
6. Covered wagon		
7. Rear-view mirror		
8. On top of the world		
9. Fancy dress		
10. Tennis ball		
11. High voltage		
12. Jump up and down		
13. Bunch of flowers		
14. Pain in the neck		
BONUS		

FIENDISH DINGBATS

*****

cross × 2

①

E E
T T
A A
D D

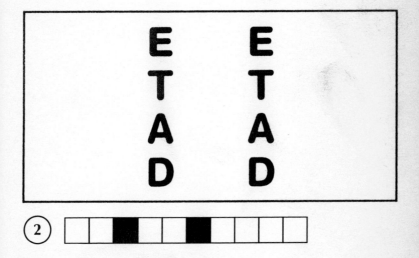

②

X bacon

3

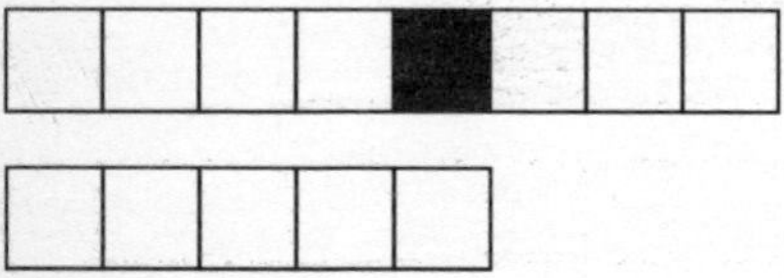

TNORF
TNORF

4

TEMPER TURE
A

(5)

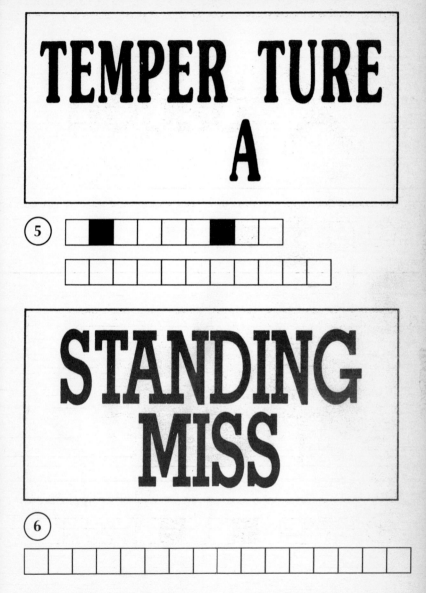

STANDING
MISS

(6)

7

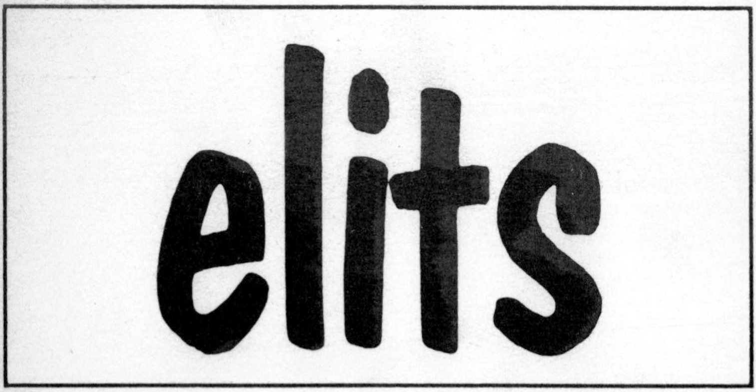

8

hump T
dump T

9

SECRET

10

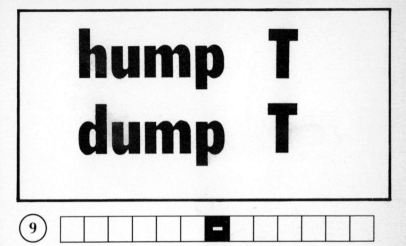

* FIENDISH DINGBATS®

(11)

(12)

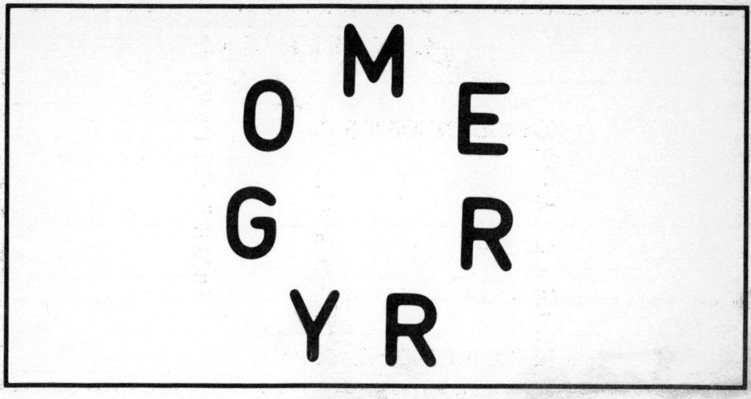

(13)

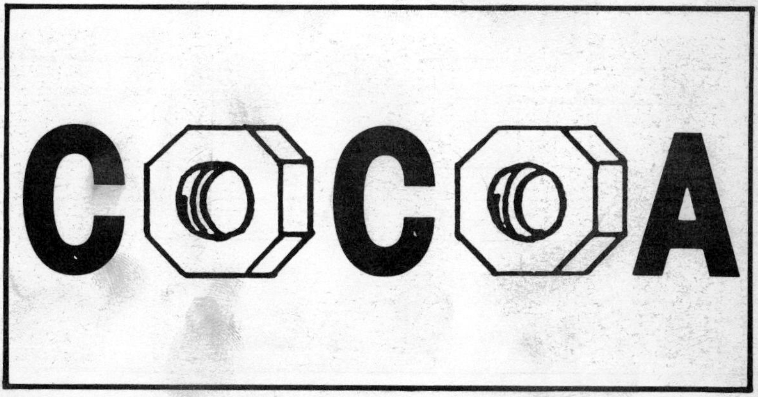

(14)

FIENDISH DINGBATS: ANSWERS

Two points

	SOLO	DUAL
1. Double-cross	☐	☐
2. Up to date	☐	☐
3. Eggs and bacon	☐	☐
4. Back-to-front	☐	☐
5. A drop in temperature	☐	☐
6. Misunderstanding	☐	☐
7. Growing old	☐	☐
8. Turnstile	☐	☐
9. Humpty-Dumpty	☐	☐
10. Top secret	☐	☐
11. Ice cube	☐	☐
12. Big Ben	☐	☐
13. Merry-go-round	☐	☐
14. Coconuts	☐	☐
BONUS	☐	☐

RAINBOW DINGBATS

*****

* RAINBOW DINGBATS®

1

2

jean jean

(3)

BRICK ROAD

(4)

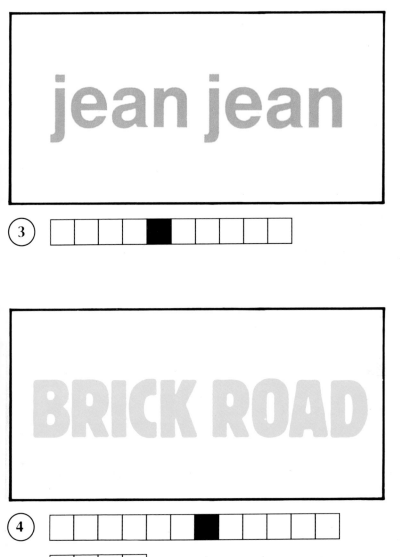

* RAINBOW DINGBATS®

STEADY GO

5

bean bean

6

boy

7

HEAD

8

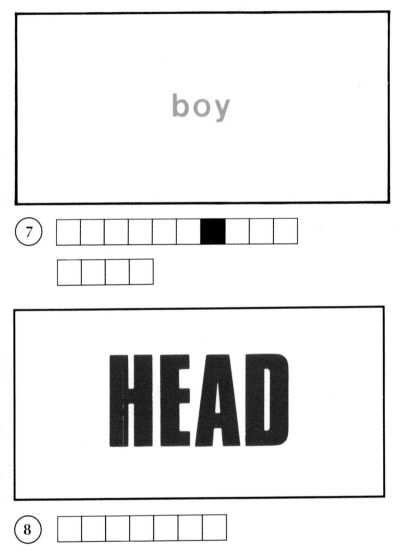

* RAINBOW DINGBATS®

WITH ENVY

9

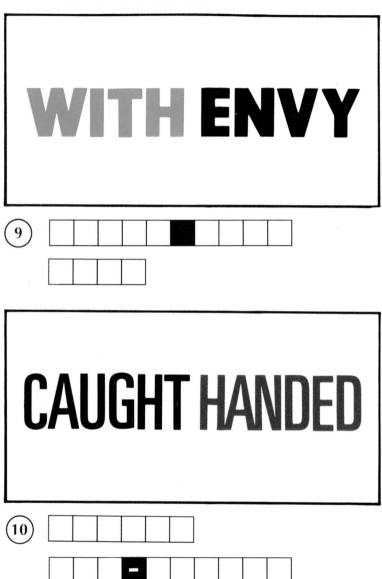

CAUGHT HANDED

10

(11)

(12)

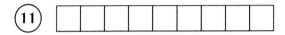

RAINBOW DINGBATS ANSWERS
One point

	SOLO	DUAL
1. Are you ready	☐	☐
2. Orange peel	☐	☐
3. Blue jeans	☐	☐
4. Yellow Brick Road	☐	☐
5. Ready, steady, go	☐	☐
6. Green beans	☐	☐
7. Little Boy Blue	☐	☐
8. Redhead	☐	☐
9. Green with envy	☐	☐
10. Caught red-handed	☐	☐
11. Evergreen	☐	☐
12. Somewhere Over the Rainbow	☐	☐
BONUS	☐	☐

DIABOLICAL DINGBATS

*****

GAME HUNTING

1

ganightle

2

* DIABOLICAL DINGBATS®

3

4

ASTRO O

(5) □□□□□□□□□

i SPY MY

(6) □■□□■□□□□

□□■□□□□□□

□□□

7 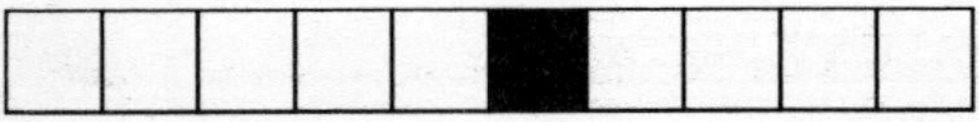

8 

(9)

(10)

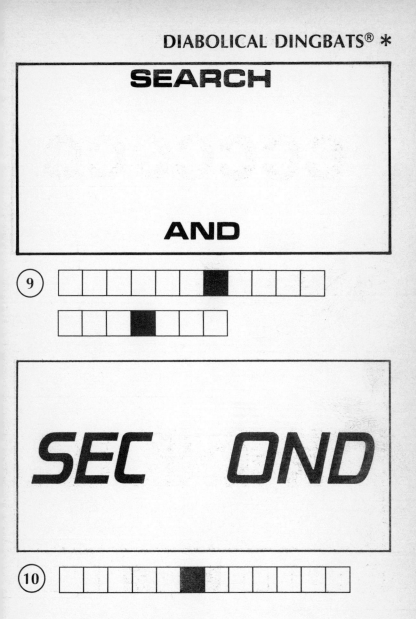

our our our our
our our our our
our our our our
our our our our
our our our our
our our our our

(11)

soil

(12)

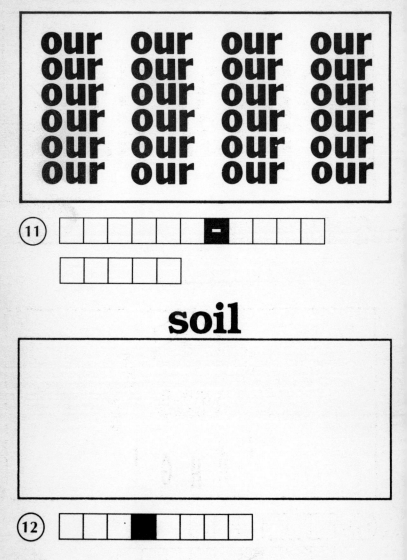

(13)

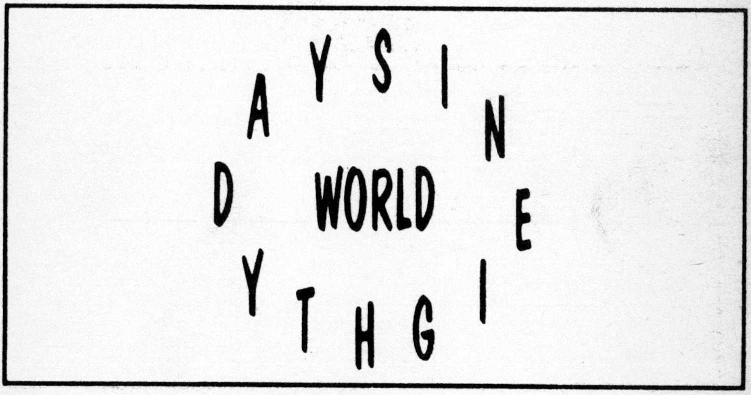

(14)

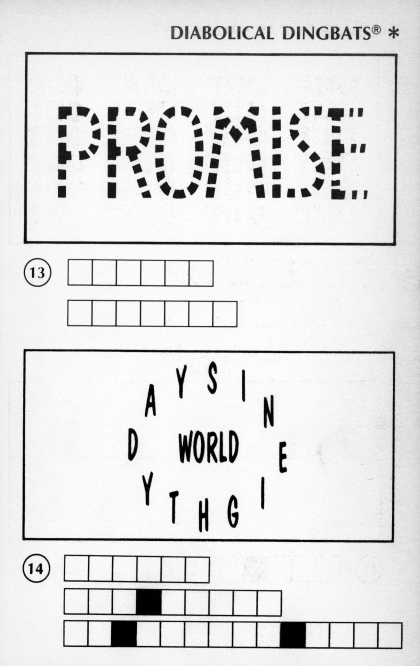

DIABOLICAL DINGBATS: ANSWERS

Three points

	SOLO	DUAL
1. Big-game hunting	☐	☐
2. Nightingale	☐	☐
3. Top of the class	☐	☐
4. Checkmate	☐	☐
5. Astronaut	☐	☐
6. I spy with my little eye	☐	☐
7. Seven Seas	☐	☐
8. Think it over	☐	☐
9. Search high and low	☐	☐
10. Split second	☐	☐
11. Twenty-four hours	☐	☐
12. Top soil	☐	☐
13. Broken promise	☐	☐
14. Around the World in Eighty Days	☐	☐
BONUS	☐	☐

YOUR DINGBATS

*****

These pages are for you to create your own Dingbats and challenge your friends.

1

2

* YOUR DINGBATS®

(3)

(4)

5

6

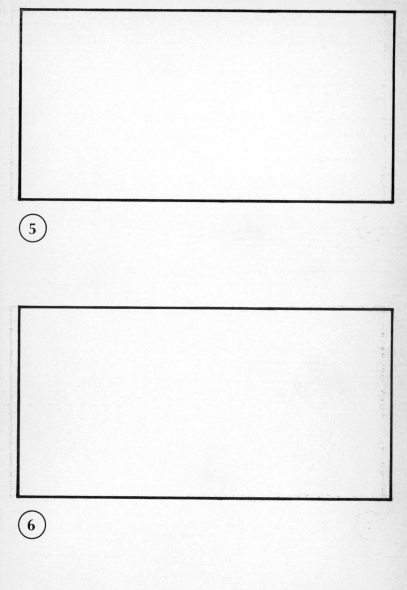

* YOUR DINGBATS®

7

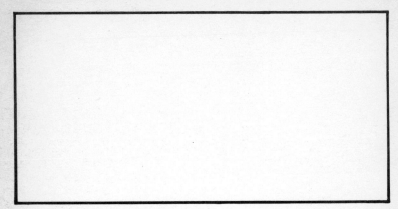

We hope you enjoyed playing the Junior DINGBATS Challenge and remember – if it's driven you crazy, we *did* warn you!

over and over again. 'We're already pushing our luck!'

Shaking his head, Luke grinds his hips against my hand one more time. 'I'm going to fucking hurt him for this,' he mutters. Then with another grunt of protest, he pushes away from me. My hand leaves his jeans and he adjusts himself as he sits up, looking like he's in pain.

'You okay there?' I'm trying not to laugh, but it's difficult.

He narrows his eyes at me. 'You think this is funny?' he asks, then slants toward me with a dark, hungry look on his face. I think he's going to kiss me, but then he says in a husky voice, 'Just wait until I get back. I'm winning the next one.' With that, he gets up, grabs his wallet from the nightstand, and tucks it into the back pocket of his jeans, looking pretty pleased with himself.

I roll onto my stomach and rest my chin in my hands as I stare at him. 'You're really going to leave me here?'

'Well, I don't really have a choice anymore,' he says, gripping the doorknob as Cole continues to bang on the door on the other side, chewing Luke out. 'I have to go now, but I probably wouldn't have let you go anyway.'

I give him a dirty look. '*Let* me go? Seriously? What is this? 1950?'

'No, I just care about you too much.' He pauses as I get out of bed and cross the room to him, noting he looks a little pale again. I saw him give himself another injection this morning, so hopefully it'll help with his paleness and exhaustion. I don't know enough about diabetes though to know for sure. I'm starting to worry more and more though. I've seen him so drunk once that he needed my help checking his blood sugar and giving him pills.

'Fine, I'll let you *make* me stay here,' I say which gets him to smile. 'Now go win big.' I press my lips to his, giving him a quick kiss, then pat his ass. 'That is how they do it on the football field, right?'

He shakes his head, trying not to laugh at me. 'Please stay out of trouble,' he says as he turns the doorknob.

Rolling my eyes, I give him a salute. 'Yes, boss.'

A contemplative look rises on his face. 'You should start calling me that more. I like it,' he says and as I shake my head he playfully pinches my side. He laughs and opens the door all the way.

Cole is standing there with his arms folded, looking annoyed, mad and drunk, amongst other things. 'I know I seem cool and everything,' he says to Luke sternly. 'But not with this. If I get you connections, you better follow through or else I'll drop you.'

I can tell it irks Luke, and he probably has to bite his tongue really hard to stay calm. 'Well, I'm ready now, so let's get going.'

Cole glares at him then glances over his shoulder at me. 'Kyler's staying if you want to go hang out downstairs with him.'

I nod while Luke scowls at Cole. 'I'll get dressed and head down.' Then I wave at Luke and shut the door before he can freak out more.

I get dressed in a tank top and jeans, wishing I'd brought shorts, but I didn't think it'd be this damn hot. Then I go downstairs to see if I can stomach any sort of food. I haven't had too many hangovers in my life, but I'm learning quickly that it makes my stomach super queasy.

When I get downstairs, Kyler is sitting at the kitchen table, eating a sandwich, music playing in the background as he plays a game of solitaire. He seems really into it, twisting around one of his eyebrow piercings, lost in deep thought. When he notices me, he fights back a grin. *Feeling better?*

I sigh and make my way over to the table. 'Yeah, sorry about last night. I get a little intense when I'm drunk.'

You were fine. He flips a card over and then studies his next move. *Amusing more than anything.*

'Well, I'm glad you think so,' I say, then point to his plate. 'Mind if I make one for myself?'

He nods, setting the cards aside and getting up. *I'll make you one.*

I shake my head and motion for him to sit back down. 'Thanks, but I'm good.' I open the fridge. 'I'm totally self-sufficient.'

Yeah, I can kind of see that. He picks up the deck, but then looks like he wants to tell me something as I get out the mayo, lunchmeat and cheese. Finally, he puts the deck of cards back down. *So how did you learn sign language anyway?* I tense and he must see it too because he adds, *You don't have to tell me if you don't want to.*

'No, it's okay . . . I guess.' I grab some bread from the loaf on the counter and a paper plate. 'I learned it from one of my foster brothers.' I don't look at him, not wanting to see his face when I reveal that I'm parentless, and keep my attention on making my sandwich. *Mayo on bread, meat, cheese, topped off with more bread and done.* When I finally turn around with the sandwich in my hand, I discover he's staring at me.

And then his hands move in front of him. *I grew up in foster homes too.*

I'm in mid-bite and it's a good excuse not to respond right away, but really I'm trying to pull myself together. This is a heavy subject, which I don't like to talk about—my time spent being passed between families. 'How come?' I finally ask after I swallow the bite as I sit down at the table.

Parents couldn't take care of me. It's signed so casually but I can see the pain emitting from his eyes.

'But you're with your dad now?' I pick some of the crust off the bread.

I know, but he didn't want me until I was eighteen and could pretty much take care of myself.

I feel bad for him. I lost my parents and was forced to live with other people. Kyler's parents gave him away by choice. 'What about your mom?'

He shrugs. *Let's just say she was never ready to be a parent . . . then again, quite honestly, I still don't think my dad even is right now. He acts like a kid sometimes and is hard to trust . . . sometimes I feel like the parent.* He pauses, shaking his head at his own thoughts. *What about you? Where are your parents?*

I hesitate. God, how the hell did I end up in this conversation? 'They died when I was five . . .' My voice cracks and I clear my throat, thinking of a subject changer.

I'm so sorry.

I shake it off, I'm getting so sick of hearing the word *sorry*. I know people mean well, but it doesn't change anything. 'I like this song,' I say, nodding at the iPod.

He gives me a questioning look, noting my need to change the subject, but lets it go. *Yeah, Taking Back Sunday is a good band. Great live, too.*

'Yeah, I saw them once a couple of years ago,' I say and take another bite of the sandwich. 'It was super badass.'

We continue on about our favorite bands, but my lips are moving almost robotically, my parents taking up most of my thoughts. I just keep thinking about what it would be like if I ended up with them again, like Kyler with his dad? Of course that can never happen, but sometimes it's good pretending, like I did for the first year or so after they died. It's actually the first time I've really thought about them without freaking out. Add the light conversation with Kyler and things are going pretty good. That is until my phone starts vibrating madly inside my pocket. There must have been a delay when the battery died because a stream of text messages comes pouring in, times varying from last night to only hours ago.

Unknown: Been thinking about u a lot and how badly I want to hurt you.

Unknown: U think ignoring me is going to make me stop. Think again.

Unknown: This shit is getting old u little cunt.

Unknown: U disgust me, being with the son of the woman who took your parents lives.

Unknown: U fucking whore. Text me back.

Unknown: Fuck u.

Unknown: If u don't text me back right now, something bad is going to happen.

Unknown: I know you're in Vegas. Hope u have fun. I'll be waiting for u when u get back.

They end, just like that. It's not an ending for me, though, but a beginning of a panic attack if I don't find a way to calm down. Because he knows where I am but the question is how? How did he find out, when hardly anyone knows I'm here? The only people who know I'm here are the ones with me . . . and Greyson.

'Shit.' I jump from the chair, cutting Kyler off. He looks up at me worriedly, mouthing *what's wrong.* But I don't answer, dialing Greyson's phone number. It rings four times and then goes straight to his voicemail, so I leave him a rushed message about calling me immediately. He could just be at work, but what if he's not? What if something happened to him . . . what if *unknown* is with him? God, I don't want to flip out, but I'm about to. Pins. Needles. Pins. Needles. They're poking madly underneath my skin.

'Can you excuse me for a second?' I ask Kyler and when he nods, I dash up to the room, unsure of what I'm going to do. At first I'm only thinking about myself and about the many ways I could hurt myself, but then all my thoughts go to Greyson. I'm worried about him. Me. Violet Hayes. Worried about someone else besides herself. Actually, I'm worried about a lot of people at the moment.

So I dial Greyson's number again, squeezing my eyes shut, and holding my breath, crossing my fingers he'll answer. 'Please, please Greyson, pick up.'

He doesn't though, so I end up dialing him ten times, over and over again, becoming like a stalker myself. Finally he picks up, though, but is very, very grumpy about it. But I'm relieved to hear his voice.

'What the hell, Violet,' he hisses in the phone. 'I'm at work, filling in for you. Remember?'

'Shit. Sorry, but it's really important.' I sit down on the bed then lie down on my back. 'Did you tell anyone that I was coming to Vegas with Luke?'

There's some clanking and banging of dishes in the background. 'Yeah, Seth. But that's it.'

'Did he tell anyone?'

'Probably. He tells everyone everything.' He pauses and I can hear the manager of the diner hollering something in the background. 'Wait? Was I not supposed to say anything to anyone?'

'No, it's fine, but . . .' I waver, wondering if I should tell him what's really going on. I hate telling my problems to people but it doesn't seem like I have a choice anymore. 'It's not really a big deal or anything, I've just been getting these weird texts and they know I'm in Vegas with Luke, which is strange since no one really knows except you and I guess Seth.'

'Texts from that reporter again?'

'I don't think so. I mean, it could be a reporter, but I don't know.' I let out a loud exhale. 'Could you do me a favor and call Seth and see who he told, just so I can maybe get an idea of who's being a douche.'

'Of course,' he says, not pressing any further. 'Give me ten minutes and I'll take a break and go call him. Then call you right back.'

'Thank you,' I say, feeling the slightest bit lighter, the pins and needles not so potent and sharp. So this is what asking for help is like? I should really do it more often, but then again, getting to the point of asking feels like pulling teeth.

'You're welcome,' he says, meaning it. 'Talk to you in just a minute.'

We hang up and I try to relax the best that I can, watching the minutes tick by, but I only breathe freely again when Greyson calls back. 'So it wasn't Seth,' he says as soon as I pick up. 'While I was talking to Seth on the phone, Benny overheard me talking about it and said that some guy called up the other day, asking where you were.'

My mouth droops to a frown. 'You told Benny where I was?'

'Well, only because I was filling in for you. But Benny doesn't know you're with Luke, so I'm not sure how they found that out. But Seth promises he hasn't said a word and he may be a gossiper but he's sure as hell not a liar. He's actually the opposite sometimes—too truthful.'

'Yeah, I know.' I sigh tiredly, wondering if the *unknown* is the one who called the diner, how he found out I was with Luke. And why it matters to the guy enough to track me down? *Who could he be? The other person there that night? Could it be fucking possible?* The idea makes my hairs stand on end. 'Thanks for finding that out.'

'No problem.' He hesitates then asks, 'Everything going okay?'

'Yeah, I guess so.' I pause, forcing myself to knock down that wall again, the one I always try to put up when people want to talk to me. 'I got super trashed last night though.'

'That doesn't sound like you.'

'I know. It was an impulsive decision that led to me crying myself to sleep while Luke cuddled me . . . I feel like a crazy asshole. Seriously. I used to be so tough and badass and now I'm a hot mess.'

'Everyone can be a hot mess sometimes. Trust me.'

'Yeah, I know, but I hate making people *have* to take care of me.'

'I'm sure Luke didn't mind, Violet,' Greyson assures me. 'In fact, he probably kind of enjoyed it, seeing as how he's in love with you.'

'We've had this conversation way too many times,' I remind him. 'Luke's not in love with me. We just have . . . well, I don't know what we have but it sure as hell isn't love.'

'You sure about that?' he questions cynically. 'Because I think you just don't want to admit that it is, because you're afraid—afraid of letting someone feel that way about you.'

'Yeah, I'm sure Mr Therapist,' I utter quietly. 'Besides, I don't even know what love is.'

Silence stretches between us, the awkward kind. We've talked a lot but I'm usually pretty closed off so I think my openness about my emotions shocked him. 'Violet, I—'

I cut him off. 'Hey, can I call you back? Luke just walked in.' A lie, but I'm not ready to have this conversation with Greyson yet and probably never.

'Yeah, sure.' He seems hurt like he knows I'm bullshitting him, which shows how much he knows me. 'Call me back, though, okay? I worry about you.'

'Yeah, absolutely,' I say and then quickly hang up, my heart racing inside my chest as I fight to catch my breath. 'I don't even know what love is? Really Violet? I need to start keeping my damn mouth shut,' I mumble to myself, sitting down on the edge of the bed and letting my head fall into my hands. For a brief instant, I try to remember what it felt like to be loved by my parents, what it felt like to be hugged, cared for, feel warm on the inside instead of hollow and cold. Surprisingly, my thoughts drift to Luke and when he calmed me down last night, right in the middle of a panic attack. No one has ever gotten me to do that before, or better yet has even tried to calm me down.

As I'm lying there, trying to sort through my emotions without wanting to fling myself out the damn window, my phone vibrates from inside my pocket. At first I think it's my stalker texter but then I realize the phone is actually ringing this time. When I see Detective Stephner's name flash across the screen, relief washes over me as I answer it.

'It's about damn time,' I say to him as I put the phone up to my ear. 'I was beginning to think you were intentionally avoiding my calls.'

'I've been busy.' Something in his voice throws me off a little. It's not that he's being rude so much as he sounds anxious.

I sit up straighter. 'Busy with what exactly?' I ask curiously.

'I can't tell you yet, not until we know for sure,' he tells me with a hint of remorse. 'But as soon as I can, I will.'

My heart hammers even harder inside my chest and I'm seriously starting to worry it's going to leap straight out. 'Is it about my parents? Did they find evidence against Mira? Or did they find the other person who did it?' My words are rushing out of my lips a hundred miles a minute as the possibilities stream through my head. *Is this it? The moment I've been waiting for? Is justice finally going to happen after all these years?*

'Violet, calm down,' he says like it's something so easy. 'I can't officially discuss anything yet, but like I said, as soon as I can, I'll call you.'

'That's not fair,' I gripe. 'You shouldn't have called me until you could talk to me.'

He sighs tiredly. 'I called because you called me, remember? You left a message about getting some texts again.'

'Oh yeah.' The adrenaline surging through me makes my voice quiver. 'At first I thought it was another reporter, but they know stuff about me that a reporter wouldn't unless they were stalking me.'

'Give me the details,' he says and I start yammering off what's been going on and even read him all the texts.

'Can you forward those to me?' he asks when I'm finished yammering. 'I'd like to have a copy.'

'Of course,' I say, already on it. 'You'll get them in just a second.'

'I want to put a trace on your phone too,' he says as I put the phone on speaker so I can still hear him, but work the message section. 'See if we can track the number the texts are coming from.'

'It comes up as unknown, though.'

'Doesn't matter. It could still be traceable.'

'How long will something like that take?'

'It all depends,' he says. 'But I'll get working on it as soon as we hang up. And if you get any more of the texts, call me immediately.' A pause. 'Violet, I have to ask about Luke. You're really with him right now like the texts are saying?'

'Yeah . . . it kind of just happened.' I suddenly feel guilty about it, especially with the way he says it, like he's disappointed. 'There was some stuff going on and . . . Look, I know who his mother is and everything but he's not a bad person.'

'I never said he was,' Stephner replies. 'I was just wondering where he was in case we need to get ahold of him for some reason.'

'Oh.' I give another long pause, knowing there's no point in asking, but I can't help it. 'Can't I have like a tiny detail about what's going on?'

'I'll try to call you in the morning,' he says, avoiding my question. 'And make sure you're with someone at all times. I don't want you wandering around by yourself until we figure out where these texts are coming from.'

'Okay, I will,' I tell him, irritated that he still won't spill the beans about whatever's going on, even though deep down I know he can't without getting into some serious trouble.

'Good.' He hesitates then adds, 'And Violet, just try to relax. I have a feeling some good things are going to be happening soon.'

I think it's his way of giving me a little hint, that whatever's going on is a good thing. At least that's the way I'm choosing to take it. And by the time I hang up on him, I feel a little lighter, like maybe soon I'll be able to breathe again, without the weight of life crushing down on me, for the very first time in almost fifteen years.

Chapter 13

Luke

Things were going good. So, so good. Violet and I were finally talking and I felt like she was really opening up to me. But I should have known it wouldn't last. You'd think I'd have learned my lesson after all this time, but I guess I'm a slow learner. Shortcuts. There's always risk when you come to them.

The good day began plummeting with the more the hours passed. It started out when I was reading more of Amy's journal and found something so fucked up, I couldn't even process it. The reason Caleb had raped her. And reading about it nearly tore me to shreds.

I was never supposed to find out about it, my sister, Amy, had written across the lined paper, the black ink smeared as if she'd been crying and the tears had dripped down to the pages. *The rape was supposed to be part of the deal. My mother owed a debt to him for drugs and had offered me to Caleb against my will and Caleb had more than gladly taken up the offer, but only if he could just take me without my consent. Just like that, my mother sold her daughter, like a pimp sells a prostitute. I was at a party when it happened. I remember Caleb had his eyes on me the entire time, everywhere I went that night, and it bothered me enough that I left the house early and went home. I knew his reputation, that he liked to be rough with girls, get them drunk and take advantage of them. He also sold drugs to my mother—I remember thinking that a lot that night and how sad it was because he was so young to be in so deep. My mother, well, she hadn't always been that way, not until my father took off and then she kind of went off the deep end, getting high all the time, her mind slipping further and further away from her. I think she might have had an underlying mental disorder to begin with and all the crack and heroin just made it worse. Maybe that's what Caleb's problem was, because why would someone ever want to do that to another person? Why would he want to follow me down the hallway and grab me from behind . . . when I tried to scream, he covered my mouth with his hand. All the lights were off in the house and Luke's door was shut, so he couldn't hear my muffled cries as Caleb dragged me toward my room. But my mom could—she could see me when she walked out of her room, the light blinding behind her, and peered into the hallway right before Caleb got me inside my room. She was wearing her robe and had this weird look on her face, relief maybe.*

'Be quiet,' she told Caleb as she tied up her robe. 'I don't want you waking up her brother.' Then she turned back into her room, shut the door, and let Caleb drag me to my bedroom, gag me and tie me up, then rape me over and over again until every part of me died inside.

My soul died that night and I'm hoping that my body will soon follow because being here is just too hard . . . too painful.

I was nearly in tears when I finished reading it, but Violet had woken up and I forced myself to pull it together. But I noticed the date of the entry in the corner when I was shutting the notebook. Two days before Amy had taken her life because she couldn't deal with the idea of living anymore in the darkness that had taken over her mind.

It made me want to throw up. How could my mother do that to her own daughter? But the real fucked-up thing was that I wasn't even as surprised as one might think and it makes me worry just how many 'surprises' are in store for me in the future.

Thankfully, through all this, I managed to keep my shit together long enough to get out of the house and away from Violet. I'd left the house, thinking things couldn't possibly get worse, when my uncle Cole up and decided that he wanted to cheat too and without warning me. The bosses of The Warehouse caught on to what we were doing and I guess it wasn't the first time it has happened with Cole.

That's when they come down and drag him toward the backroom. I'm right in the middle of a winning hand and just like that, there's all this commotion. Cole puts up a fight as two guys grab an arm each and pull him across the open warehouse. I'm getting to my feet, trying to figure out what to do, whether I should go after him, when a large, overweight guy with a thick neck, dressed head-to-toe in black, comes up to me.

'Follow me,' he says and when I hesitate adds, 'It'll be worse if you don't.'

Grinding my teeth, I set the cards down on the table and follow the guy as he makes his way past the poker tables toward this back area hidden behind a steel wall. By the time I get in there, the two guys that hauled my uncle off are beating the shit out of him, one holding him by the arms while the other rams his fist into Cole's gut, face, arms—everywhere.

'Hey,' I start to protest when I'm shoved face-first to the floor by a heavy set of hands and end up bashing my face on the concrete. The taste of blood fills my mouth and my jaw starts to throb as I go to push up, but a foot comes down and holds me in place. They take my wallet out of my pocket, I'm sure to take all the cash I have in there. It's not everything, but it's enough that I'm in deep shit. Not to mention all I won tonight is gone.

'And if you come back here again,' one of the guys says to Cole as he slams his fist right into his face, blood spurting from his mouth and landing on the floor, 'Greford won't let you walk out of here.'

The foot moves from my back as they let go of my uncle and he falls to the floor, unable to even hold his head up. I push up and start to head to him, when one of the guys comes at me.

I shove him back roughly. 'Don't even fucking think about it. This has nothing to do with me.'

'Oh you think so,' the guy says. He has this gnarly scar going round his eye and this sick look in his eyes as he wipes some of my uncle's blood off his chin. 'You come here with a cheater, you're declared a cheater.

Rules of the game.' Then he cranes his arm back and rams his fist into my jaw, right on the side that hit the concrete.

Instinctively I react with a ram of my own fist, hitting him right in the side. It shocks him a little and then suddenly I'm being held back and the scar guy sucker punches me three or four more times before he lets me go.

My whole body hurts, but the pain is minimal compared to the reality of the situation. My uncle unconscious, no money, no way to pay Geraldson back.

'Now get your goddamn asses out of here,' Scar guy says and then spits on the floor in front of me before leaving with the other guys.

Stumbling to my feet, I stagger my way over to my uncle, bruised, beaten, and broken, ready to give up. When I roll him over, he looks dead—bloody, his face swollen, his nose a purplish blue. But then he opens his eyes and gives a cough. 'Well, damn. That sucks.' No apology. No excuses. No nothing.

Annoyed and sore as hell, I help him to his feet and get him to the car. He gives me the keys, unable to drive with one of his eyes swelled shut and I hop in the driver's seat and head back to the house, my mind racing a million miles a minute. *Fuck, I'm fucked.* This is the thought that's running over and over in my mind as I drive.

'Should I . . . should I maybe take you to the emergency room?' I finally ask, feeling my own body ache with the need to be treated.

He shakes his head, turning toward the window, mumbling, 'There's a warrant for my arrest and the last thing I want to do is get caught.'

'For what?' I ask, merging onto the freeway.

'That's none of your business.' He rests his head on the window and stays quiet for the rest of the drive.

After we get to the house, I help him inside and can't help but think of my own future and wonder if this is where I'm headed. Twenty years old and I've already had my ass kicked more than I can remember for getting caught cheating. And now I have no money to pay back Geraldson. I'm wondering if that's how Cole was? From what I can remember, even when I was five years old and he would have been twenty, he was gambling, drinking and fighting, the same way he is now.

By the time we stumble into the foyer it's late, well past midnight. There's a lamp on in the living room, but the rest of the house is dark, so I make my way in there, Cole's arm around my shoulder as I bear most of his weight with my own battered body.

'Easy,' he mutters to me as I manoeuver us down the step and through the doorway toward the sofa.

When we enter, Kyler, who's sitting on the couch watching television, instantly looks over at us. He sets his beer down and doesn't seem the least bit shocked at the sight of us, only annoyed with his father and the condition he's in, which looks even worse now, all the places he was hit swelled up to twice as bad as when we left The Warehouse. Kyler signs something short and simple, his movements clipped.

'Hey, you were the one who decided not to go tonight,' Cole says as he slowly lowers himself down onto the chair beside the sofa and slips his arm off my shoulder. 'You know I do these things when you're not around—I can't help myself.'

Kyler glances from me to his father then signs something again and even though I don't know sign language, the movements of his arms are enough for me to tell he's said something harsh.

'Hey, Luke asked me to help him,' Cole protests, touching his puffy cheek with his fingertips then wincing. There's blood splattered all over his torn shirt and I'm fairly certain his nose is broken. 'That's what

I was trying to do. If I hadn't got caught, then Luke wouldn't have had to share his winnings with me and would have had enough to pay his debt.'

'I didn't ask you to do that,' I tell him, not wanting to be rude, but I don't want the blame for this, nor did I ever want to lose all my money and be back to square one. 'I would have been fine with playing another night or two. Now I have nothing and no game to go to.'

'I'll find us another place,' Cole promises, reclining back in the chair and putting his feet onto the table. He's lost his shoes somewhere—who knows where. 'I just need a few days.' He shuts his eyes and lets his head tip back.

'I don't have a few days.' I rub my hand down my face then wince, forgetting that my cheek is injured. 'I'm so fucked.'

'We'll figure it out. Nothing I haven't handled before,' Cole mumbles while Kyler shoots a glare at his dad and throws the beer cap at him to get him to open his eyes. When he does, Kyler mouths something, but I can't catch what. 'Hey, I'm good at figuring stuff out under pressure,' Cole tells Kyler then looks up at me. 'You think maybe you could ask your dad to spot us some cash so we can get things moving again?'

I shake my head and back away. 'I'm not asking my father for anything.'

He frowns. 'Luke, it might be our only option.'

I hate the way he says *our* option as if his problem has become my problem. 'I have enough problems of my own,' I tell him. 'I don't need any more.'

'Just think about it,' Cole says while Kyler shakes his head, irritated, as if his father does this all the time and Kyler is tired of it. 'I'm sure he would do it for you if you asked him.'

Even if I wanted to ask him, I'm not so sure he would or if he has access to that kind of money. But I don't want to go down that road with my father anyway, so it's not an option. 'I'm leaving tomorrow morning,' I tell Cole then leave the room. He calls out my name, almost panicking, but I know it's not over me. It's over himself. He's a gambling addict. Pure and simple. My possible future, if I don't figure out a way to straighten my act up. What a fucking wake-up call. Though I'm not sure why it happened: if it had something to do with finding out the truth about what happened to Amy, or if it was Violet opening up to me and making me want to be a better person.

As I tiredly drag my sore ass up the stairs, I try to remember how I got to this point in time, how I messed up my life so badly. Tired. Beat up. Broke. Alone. The last one might not be so true anymore. That's really up to Violet and whether she'll ever have me again. Honestly, she'd be better off without me, at least until I clean my act up, but I'm too selfish to walk away from her.

That's what I'm trying to convince myself not to be—selfish—when I enter the room and see her lying in bed, the covers kicked down, wearing one of my shirts, her long legs stretched out, and I realize I need her. Through the insanity of my life, Violet is the one sane thing I have, even if our relationship is insane itself.

She's left a lamp on, so there's a soft trail of light in the small room. I tug my shirt off and slip my boots off as I make my way to the bed, pausing when I get beside it to unbutton my jeans and take them off. Her back is to me, her head resting against the pillow, her hair loose and down her back. I reach forward and brush it aside, then trace my fingertips along the two stars on her neck, her skin so soft and familiar, everything I want.

I can barely remember the first time I ever had sex and all the times after are a blur until I met Violet. Sure, it always felt good, for me at least. Not sure about the women since I didn't care nor did I stick around long enough to ask. There was something about having that kind of control over a person like that—where I could just walk away before they ever used me—that made me feel briefly content. It would always fade though, eventually, and I'd only get the contentment again when I fucked the next one and so on and so on. I've never actually been with anyone more than once, including Violet, but not because I used her and bailed like with the rest of the women I've been with. Violet has always been different from anyone else I've been with. I knew that the first moment she literally fell into me. At the time, I didn't know what exactly made her different or why I had the sudden need to be around the same woman for more than an hour. But now I think I know.

Because I'm in love with her. But I can't tell her that. Not yet. I'm not ready and neither is she. In fact, I'm not sure she'll ever be ready for that, at least with me, but I want to stick around and find out—be there for her.

Sucking a deep breath over the terrifying revelation to myself, I climb into the bed and press up against her, wrapping my arms around her, slipping one underneath the crook of her neck so her head is resting on my arm like a pillow. I feel her jump a little and I half expect her to wake up out of her nightmare and be in panic, like she normally is whenever she wakes up. But she must have been awake the entire time, because she barely stirs before she relaxes.

'You smell like cigars,' she mutters as my fingers drift up and down her side. 'And beer.'

I pull her closer against me and breathe in her scent; something vanilla with a hint of perfume that makes me briefly shut my eyes and get lost. 'You look good in my shirt,' I whisper, opening my eyes, then I brush her hair out of the way and kiss the sensitive spot on her neck, right below her jawline, letting my lips linger there to suck the taste of her skin.

'Luke . . .' She almost sounds torn, her fingers finding my arm and digging into my skin. I wait for her to pull away, stop us from doing something, but then her back curves in and her ass presses against my cock.

The contact of it makes me groan and bite down on her skin more roughly than I intended on doing. In response, her nails stab into my skin, her back arching even more as my knee slides between her legs and I slip my hand up underneath her shirt to grip her hip, her skin warm.

'God, you feel so good . . .' I trail off as I start

sucking on her neck and rubbing my knee against her while she begins rocking her hips with my movements, causing my cock to go rock hard. I could seriously be content with this, just touching her, which is frightening that I don't need to take more, even though I want it. Need is so much different than want. Need is something driven by an addiction while want is something *I* want to do. Want. I want Violet.

She must think the opposite though because suddenly she's slipping out from my hold. My eyes widen as she moves away from me, but then she turns around, climbing on top of me and straddling me. Reaching for the collar of her shirt, she yanks it over her head and tosses it onto the floor, strands of her red and black hair falling to her bare shoulders. She's not wearing a bra or panties and when her nipples hit the air they instantly get hard, which makes my cock instantly get more eager.

'Fuck, baby, I . . .' I trail off. I've never had a girl take control like this before. Usually I'm the one that is . . . needing the control. And it's hard not to grab her and flip her over, take over things, but I manage to stay put beneath her and see where this goes.

A small smile touches her lips as she places her hands on my shoulders and pins me down to the mattress. 'I think you were going to say something along the lines of I win.' Then she reaches down and grabs my jeans from off the floor. Before I can ask her what she's doing, she sits back up and puts a condom down on my chest.

'How did you know what was in there?' I ask, picking up the condom.

She shrugs, brushing her hair out of her eyes. 'I just assumed.'

I frown. 'You know I haven't been with anyone since you, right?'

'I wouldn't blame you if you did,' she says. 'We weren't together.'

'Well, I haven't.' And it's the truth. Sure I've thought about messing around, taking my mind off stuff, but going through with it was too hard and always thinking of Violet would put an end to it before things ever got too far.

'I guess you're a little deprived then.' She rocks her hips, rubbing her wetness against my cock. Jesus, I swear she knows exactly how to get under my skin, in the best fucking way possible.

Something snaps inside me, something that I've never felt before. And I feel even more helpless when she starts to lower herself down on me, slipping my dick inside her. Halfway down, I can't take it anymore and with one hard thrust of my hips, I slam myself against her and thrust my cock deep inside her.

She immediately winces and bites down on her lip, her muscles tight around me. I freeze, suddenly remembering that she's only had sex once, and that was two months ago. She's still tight as hell and I was rough. Really, really fucking rough.

'Shit, did I hurt you,' I ask, sweeping some of her hair out of her face as her fingernails stab into my shoulders.

She shakes her head, the pain in her expression shifting to pleasure as she rolls her hips. 'No . . . it feels good, just a little intense . . . it's been a while . . .' She repeats the movement over and over again with her hips, going slowly, as if she's savoring the sensations, her hands going to her shoulders and she runs her fingers down her body.

It's driving me crazy, watching her eyes gloss over, her lips part as she presses down on me, touching herself, totally in control. Finally, I lose it again and start moving with her, thrusting my hips upward, my hands finding her waist and holding on. I move slow at first, but then get faster, harder, rougher the more she moans. Her grip on me loosens as her head starts to fall back and I sit up, still holding onto her and moving, so I can press my lips to hers. She kisses back briefly, but is so lost in the moment, she ends up biting down on my bottom lip.

'Harder,' she gasps, pressing against me as I rock into her, our movements matching perfectly. 'Oh God . . . please . . . harder . . .'

I'm terrified beyond imagination. Seriously. I can't think about anything else but her. Every single part of me belongs to her at that moment. I feel something change inside me, something that makes me want to be a better person forever.

I love you, I want to say. My problems are momentarily forgotten. Life is momentarily forgotten. And all I can do is hold on and hope I never have to let go.

Violet

Holy hell, this is way, way better than the first time I had sex. Less painful. More intense. But I think that might be because Luke is letting go more this time instead of being careful with me.

I'm on top of him, clutching onto his shoulders, while he sits up and thrusts deep inside me, the movement of my hips matching his. One of his hands is gripping at my waist, while the other rests at the base of my neck, putting gentle pressure against my flesh as he holds onto me and kisses me with so much passion I can barely breathe.

We keep moving and moving, getting more lost in each other, our skin beading with sweat as we become breathless, exhausted, but it feels way too good to stop—I never want it to stop. And he seems to feel the same way too, savoring each kiss, grip, bite, each brush of our skin and the uniting of our bodies until we both fall helplessly into bliss at the same time.

I cry out in sheer pleasure, the sound of my voice unrecognizable as my fingers stab at his skin in desperation, needing to hold onto something. Luke keeps thrusting into me a few moments longer before he starts to slow, pressing one last time deep inside of me as his head collapses against my chest.

He remains still for a while, breathing heavily against my chest, like he's afraid to move. I kind of don't want him to either, because everything feels perfect right now, which is rare for me, if nonexistent. But eventually he shifts back down, slipping out of me, but bringing me with him and pulling me against him as we lie in the bed, face to face. As the lamp casts the light over his cheek, I realize there's a massive lump there, on top of a preexisting bruise and a little bit of dried blood. I was so caught up in the intimate moment, I didn't realize it was there until now.

'What happened?' I ask, gently placing my hand over the injury. 'Did you get in a fight?'

He shrugs, eyes on mine as he leans into my touch as if my hand is soothing him. 'A little one, but nothing too major.'

'Did you get caught cheating?'

His breath falters from his lips. 'Cole did, but it's not that big of a deal. I don't owe any money or anything.'

His voice is off pitch and all that peace we had moments ago shatters into a million pieces I so want to put back together again. 'They took the money, didn't they?' I ask with a frown.

He doesn't answer my question, only uttering, 'I'll figure something out.' He blows out a tired breath and then rubs his eyes, appearing worn out.

'I want to help,' I tell him, tracing the lines of one of his tattoos on his ribcage. 'Let me help.'

'I'm not going to let you deal drugs to help me,' he says in a clipped tone, shaking his head. 'I'd rather get the shit beat out of me than have you do that and owe *him*.' His expression softens a little as he puts a hand on my back and gently sketches his finger up and down my spine. 'Let me sleep on it. I might have an idea, but I need to figure out how desperate I am.'

I don't know what his idea is, but it worries me, because the last time I saw that look of pure helplessness on his face was the night he told me that his mother could possibly be my parents' killer.

Chapter 14

Luke

I watch her sleep for most of the night. Thinking. My head so cluttered I can barely breathe. By the time I'm actually finished the sun is coming up and I've had absolutely no sleep whatsoever. It's been that way for the last couple of months and between that and the drinking, I'm starting to feel the effects of it on my body. Constantly tired, I wonder how I'm ever going to survive football season if I don't get my act together.

My act together. It seems like I have so much to do before that can ever be possible, but as I lie here looking at Violet asleep in my arms, I want to do it more than anything.

As the sun rises higher and lights up the room, I decide to take the first step, even though I don't want to at all.

I begrudgingly get out of bed and grab my phone to make a call I never thought I could make in a million years. But the alternative, staying here until I can figure something else out, isn't something I want to do anymore.

It's still early in California, but my dad answers after three rings. 'Luke, is everything okay?'

I swear to God it's like he knows I need something. 'Not really.' I pause, waiting for him to say something but he doesn't as I stare out the window. 'Look, I need a favor . . . I need to borrow some money.' If he turns me down again, I don't think I can ever ask him for anything.

'Okay.' He already sounds wary. 'How much do you need?'

I glance over my shoulder as Violet stirs in the bed, then make my way over to the bathroom attached to the room and go inside so I don't wake her up. 'Nine grand.'

He lets out a slow, low whistle. 'Shit, Luke. That's a lot of money.'

'I know it is.' I shut the door, lean against it, and slide to the floor. 'I wouldn't be asking if it wasn't an emergency.'

'Are you in some kind of trouble?'

'You could say that.' I hesitate, not sure I want to

tell him, not wanting to give him the right of knowing me yet, but then suddenly there's all this pressure inside my chest and it explodes without warning. Everything comes pouring out of me. And not just the gambling part. I tell him how much I drink. What happened between Violet and I. Everything my mom did. Even what I found in Amy's journal. And by the end I'm crying, like a scared little boy. It makes me feel so pathetic. So weak. So out of control, like when I lived with my mother, and part of me hates myself, but the other part feels relieved, like it can breathe again.

'Luke, we're going to fix this,' my dad says after I finally stop sobbing long enough for him to speak again.

'You can't fix it,' I say, sucking back the tears. 'Not most of it anyway.'

'Well, I'm going to fix what I can,' he says so calmly. I don't even know how he's doing it. I just piled twenty years of baggage onto him and he's cool as can be. 'And the rest we'll figure out together.' He pauses as if he's collecting himself. 'The first thing I'm going to do is wire you the money. You can head back to Laramie and it should be there by the time you get there. Then you'll pay back this Geraldson guy.'

I wipe the tears from my eyes with the back of my hand. 'And then what?'

'And then I want you to come visit me,' he says and before I can protest, he adds, 'Just for a week, so we can talk and maybe get to know each other a little bit better . . . I'd like to get to know my son.'

'You think talking is going to help?' I ask. 'Because I'm not so sure.'

'I think it's a step . . . and if you'll let me, I'd like to take that step with you and hopefully more steps.' He sighs. 'I know I haven't been there for you and I can't make up for the past.' Now he sounds like he's choking up. 'But I'd like to try my damn hardest. You just need to let me try.'

'I have football practice starting in a couple of weeks,' I say. 'And classes. It's hard for me to go somewhere right now.'

'Can you take some time off?' he asks, hopeful. 'Just a week or so.'

'I hate taking time off. And I've already missed more than I'm comfortable with.' I'm being a pain in the ass, still uneasy about the whole thing. Well, more like frightened. When I was younger, it was all I thought about, all those times during the needles, hugs, petting, madness. That he would come back and save me, but he never did and I nearly rotted to death in that house. And now, it's hard to let that all go.

'Then I'll come to you,' he says determinedly. 'If you say it's okay, I'll fly out there and see you.'

I run my hand over my head, letting out a stressed breath. 'How long would you stay?'

'As long as you want me to,' he replies. 'I'd take a few hours at this point.'

'That's a far flight for a couple of hours.'

'No, it's not.' The way he says it makes me want to cry again, but I suck the tears back before they spill out.

'Fine, you can come out if you want.' I push myself to my feet. 'And you can stay for a few days.'

It takes him a second to respond and when he finally does, I can tell he's crying but trying not to let me hear it. 'Good. I'm so glad. I'm so, so glad.'

It feels so strange and unbelievable, letting stuff go that I've been carrying around forever. I just hope that it all works out, but I'm not holding my breath just yet.

Chapter 15

Violet

When I wake up, Luke's not in the bed and I have this strange moment when I panic, not just because Luke isn't there beside me but also over the way I wake up. My usual gasping ritual is absent, instead my eyes simply open and all I can think is: *What the hell?*

It's more frightening than anything. I've been waking up that way and now suddenly I'm not. It feels like a part of me has gone missing and I don't know what to do with it.

And then my text goes off and makes things worse.

Unknown: Why did you call the police? U fucking cunt. You're so dead.

I'm trying not to flip out as I read the message over, when Luke walks out of the bathroom. I take one look at him, though, and the problem gets lost. He's still in his boxers, his hair ruffled, his jaw scruffy, and his eyes red and puffy—either he's stoned or he's been crying. I'm guessing it's the latter.

'What's the matter?' I sit up quickly, the blanket falling from my chest. I'm still naked from last night and his gaze flickers to my chest, but only for an instant then he rubs his eyes and sighs.

'I called my dad.' He stares down at the floor, a crease at his brow, confused. 'I couldn't think of anything else to do, so I called him and asked him for the money.'

'What'd he say?' I know very little about Luke and his dad's relationship, other than they don't have one and Luke has had no interest in having one with him because of his absence during his childhood, so if he asked him for help then it's a huge deal.

He scratches at the back of his neck, exhaling before looking at me. 'He said he would, but I have to let him visit me.'

I set the phone aside on the nightstand and swing my legs over the edge of the bed. 'He blackmailed you?'

'No, not really. He just said he'd give me the money and that he wanted to come see me and I kind of just agreed.' He sits down on the bed beside me. 'This is so weird.'

Not knowing what else to do, I scoot closer and rub his back. 'I'm sorry,' I say. 'But I'm glad he's helping you, instead of you trying to gamble again.' My words are shocking. Usually, I crave danger, but I'm discovering that if danger means Luke getting hurt it's not thrilling at all.

'Yeah, I guess I am, too.' He lowers his head into his hands. 'But we'll see how it goes. I'm not going to go into this hopeful or anything.' He sits that way for a while, with his head down, breathing softly—I think he might be trying not to cry.

I stay quiet and keep rubbing his back until finally he raises his head back up, trying to discreetly wipe the tears away from his eyes. He clears his throat a few times and then gets to his feet, grabbing a pair of jeans from his bag. 'I think we should get going,' he tells me. 'The last thing I want to do is stay here with Cole. The guy is in a way worse state than me.' He pulls his jeans on and does up the button. 'Which says a lot.'

I nod, then climb out of bed and go over to my bag, his eyes following me the entire way. 'I'm actually anxious to get back too,' I say, grabbing a shirt and pair of black pants. 'I talked to Detective Stephner last night and even though he wouldn't tell me anything,

I could tell there was something going on with the case.' I stand up and slip into the pair of black jeans. 'I'm hoping it's good.'

'When will you know?' he asks, pulling a red shirt over his head.

I shrug then slip my own shirt on and flip my hair out of the collar. 'I'm not sure. He said he might call me this morning but all I got was another text from stalker guy.'

He frowns. 'Did you tell the detective about those?'

I nod. 'He's looking into it.'

He presses his lips together as if he wants to say something, but then thinks against it and starts wandering around the room, picking up his stuff and packing his bag. I start packing too, not bothering to fold my clothes. It's actually a habit I picked up from when I was young. After packing for the fifth time to change homes, I gave up and just stuffed everything in it. And didn't bother unpacking when I got to my new home.

'You think it's about my mom?' Luke asks so suddenly it throws me off guard and takes me a moment to respond. 'What the detective can't tell you yet? Do you think it has something to do with my mom?'

I zip up my bag and pick it up. 'I wonder . . . maybe.'

'I hope it is,' he says, anger lacing his tone. I know that he means it—that he wants her locked up just as much as I do. He swings the bag over his shoulder, his muscles jerking a little as if they're sore. Then he walks up to me and gives me a soft kiss on the cheek.

'You ready?' he asks, tucking a strand of my hair behind my ear and looking me steadily in the eye. It seems like he's asking me much more than if I'm ready to leave his uncle's house. Like if I'm ready to go back to Laramie. To live with him.

I nod, not sure which question I'm answering, but I guess I'll find out when we get there.

Luke's uncle seems really upset when we walk downstairs to leave, arguing with Luke over wanting to call his father and borrow some money. Luke says nothing about the fact that he has, I guess deciding to let Cole clean up his own mess. Irate, Cole stumbles over to the coffee table in the living room and chugs about half a bottle of vodka. 'To ease the pain of the beating,' he says when he notices us all watching him. Then he plops down on the sofa and moments later he passes out.

Kyler seems like he almost wants to come with us, just to get out of the house, lingering in the foyer as

Luke drops his bag onto the floor to give him one of those awkward one-armed hugs guys do.

'You can come hang out with us whenever,' Luke says, pulling back and picking up his bag, his eyes drifting to the living room where Cole's on his back, his arm dangling over the side of the sofa. 'Even if it's just for a break.'

Kyler smiles and lifts his hands, *What the hell would I do in Wyoming?*

Luke looks to me for translation and when I pass along the message, he says, 'The university's pretty cool there.'

He raises his pierced eyebrow, amused. *Me go to school? That's a funny idea. I barely made it through high school.*

'Hey, I was the same way. In fact, I almost dropped out,' I tell him with a smile, feeling strange that I'm talking about my past so lightly. 'And I actually like college.'

Really? he mouths and I nod. He pauses, looking back at his dad who was never there for him growing up, beaten up and passed out drunk on the sofa and then mouths to me, *Maybe one day.*

I nod then he gives Luke and me his phone number and we finish saying good-bye. Then we hit the road.

It's early, the sky glowing orange from the sunrise, which means we should get there before sunset. We're a few days earlier than we planned, which means I'll be missing less class and I think Luke and I can both appreciate the fact. We spend half the drive listening to his music and he playfully tells me he's going to make us a fuck tape of our own when we get home. He keeps saying *we* and I know I should be grateful, that I have a place to live with people who care about me, but it's scaring me at the same time. *God, if I could just have one more moment with my parents so they could tell me that this is all okay. That I'm doing the right thing.*

As I'm in the middle of this thought, my phone starts to vibrate from inside my pocket. I quickly turn down the music and take out my phone, letting out a breath of relief when I see the screen. 'It's the detective,' I tell Luke and he nods, looking as nervous as me.

'Please say you can tell me now,' I say as I put the phone up to my ear.

'I can, but it's both good and bad news,' he tells me, sounding a bit disheartened. 'The good news is we finally got that warrant to search Mira Price's home. And we found something that could be potentially useful but we still need to run some DNA tests right now to confirm.' He hesitates. 'And then there's the bad news. Two bad newses actually.'

'That's not even a word.' I make a joke to attempt to hide my true feelings. That I'm excited and terrified at the same time. They might have evidence. My parents might finally have justice.

Luke gives me a sideways glance as he steers the truck down the freeway. 'Is everything okay?' he whispers.

I shrug and whisper back, 'I'll let you know in a minute.'

'Well, I'm declaring it a word for this conversation,' Stephner says and then sighs, losing all humor. 'The first bad news is that Mira is MIA and from talking to the neighbors and landlord, she's been gone for a while.'

I glance over at Luke, wondering if he might know where she is. 'So what does that mean?'

'It means that even if we can make the arrest, we have to find her first.'

I want to hit something. Scream until my lungs burst. *This isn't fair! This isn't fair. God dammit!* 'And what's the second?' My voice shakes as my pulse hammers.

It takes him a second or two to answer and when he does, he sounds reluctant. 'We found out who's been sending those texts to you . . . We tracked the calls to Preston Parkington, the guy you've been living with.'

'What?' I exclaim, ready to bombard him with questions and Luke's head whips into my direction. 'But that's not even possible . . . how could he . . . I don't get it . . .' What the hell? Is this my punishment? For messing up?

'It gets worse,' Detective Stephner says. 'Due to the threatening material of the texts, we have the right to go to his house and question him, but the trailer had been vacated when we got there.'

'But he was just living there a few days ago . . . I was there . . . I saw him.' My heart is thrashing in my chest, my pulse soaring a million miles a minute and I hate the adrenaline rush inside me right now, so much. 'He has to be doing this to get back at me, because I left.'

'That's what I maybe thought too, but then I started doing some research on him, a background check and what not, and found out a few things that have brought up a big concern.'

'Like what?'

'Like he has a record. The fact that he changed his name about fourteen years ago. He used to go by Danny Huntersonly.'

'But why would he change his name?' I shake my head, trying to ignore Luke's worried look boring into the side of my head. 'And why would child services ever let him take me in?'

'Well, technically the papers state that his girlfriend took you in. A Kelley Arlingford was registered with the state as a foster parent.'

'Kelley was his wife.' I grip the door handle for support because I'm veering toward hyperventilation and feel like I'm going to pass out. 'When she introduced him to me, she said Preston was her husband.'

'Well, she was lying to you then, and to the state apparently,' he says. 'In your records, Kelley lived alone and the state didn't even know about Preston, at least from the reports. It's kind of a flaw in the system I guess, not making sure there was no one living with her. But when children get to be that old . . . and there's so many of them . . . sometimes they slip through the cracks.'

He's telling me stuff I already know, since I lived in those cracks for years. 'Did Kelley know about Preston? I mean, did she know about his name change and past?'

'I don't know, but we're going to try and find out.' Another pause. 'There's more.'

'Oh God.' My head falls forward and Luke's hand slides across the seat, his fingers lace through mine, and I hold onto him for dear life. 'I don't think I can take any more.'

'You need to hear this,' he says. 'You need to understand the severity.'

'Fine.' I clutch onto Luke's hand so tightly I'm sure it hurts. 'Go ahead.'

'Did you know Preston had a secret room under his house?'

'Yeah . . . well, no . . .' Shit. What do I say? That I knew he kept drugs there. 'Well, he kept it locked but I knew that it existed.'

'I figured, considering what was in there.'

'Which was what?'

Another pause. I'm beginning to hate the silences. 'A room with pictures and articles of you all over the wall . . . even some of your parents.'

'I don't understand . . . why would he have that?' I mean, I know he wanted me and everything but that seems like the move of a stalker . . . 'Why is he doing this? It doesn't make any sense.' I mean, he was always a little weird and controlling, but why all of a sudden would he resort to threatening texts and a crazy room full of pictures?

He sighs again and I prepare myself for another blow to the gut. 'Violet, I'm not sure how much you know about your parents, but back in the beginning of the case there were a few suggestions that no one ever really mentioned to you, simply because you were too young and honestly we didn't want it getting out to the public. Keeping certain details a secret can better help us convict the right person. However, now I think you might need to know, but I want you to prepare yourself for it.'

'Okay, I'm prepared.' Biggest lie I ever told and I wouldn't have had the guts to say it if I had known what he was going to say next.

'During the first investigation of your parents, the lead detective on the case found some details about your parents—well, your mother anyway—that connected them to a few local drug dealers. It was a past thing, I think that ended a few years after you were born, when your mother married your father.'

'No, my mother married my dad before I was born,' I say, but really I have no idea—I barely know anything about them, having lost them at such a young age.

'No, she married him when you were about three years old,' he says. 'After she got her act together and got out of rehab, but her past was still chasing her and she owed the wrong people some money. The police were never quite able to track down the people in question, but from Preston's previous records, he was living in that area at the time and dealing drugs . . .

and some of the pictures he had of you . . . you were younger.'

'No . . . you're fucking lying.' I shake my head over and over until I get so dizzy. 'You're lying, you're lying, you're lying. I didn't live with my parents' killer. That would never happen.' *Unless it was done on purpose? Oh my God, was it somehow done on purpose?*

'I'm not saying he's their killer in any way, shape or form,' he says in a gentle voice. 'I just wanted you to know the details just in case.'

Just in case what?

Just in case what?

Just in case what?

The words echo inside my head over and over again until suddenly I'm seeing Preston's face in the memory, the one where I'm in the basement and he's yelling at Mira Price while she sings and sings and sings. So clearly. But is it just because it was suggested or did I finally put the pieces together?

'No! My mom never did drugs . . . they were good people . . .' And to me, the five-year-old with beautiful dreams, they were. They were perfect. And I want to remember them that way. I want to erase everything he said, forget I ever heard it, but I can't.

'I'm not saying they were bad,' he tells me. 'People

that do drugs aren't necessarily bad people. The just made some bad choices and your mother cleaned up her act. She just struggled to erase her past.'

Like mother like daughter.

I can't breathe. Can't think. Can't see. Everything is spinning, round and round and round. All mixed up. All wrong. I can feel the truck pulling over as I gasp for air. As soon as it stops, I drop the phone, open the door and fall out of the truck onto my knees. Gravel splits them open and the palms of my hand as I dry heave, gasping for air my lungs won't give me.

Adrenaline overload. One I didn't cause. But one that feels like it's going to kill me. And honestly, I wish it would.

Chapter 16

Luke

She's scaring the shit out of me. She won't talk. Will barely move. I have to lift her back into the truck. Once I get her inside and get the door shut I climb in the driver's side and pick up her phone off the seat, which has been ringing since she dropped it.

'Hello?' I answer, my arm moving around Violet as she lowers herself down onto the seat and puts her head on my lap. She clutches onto my jeans, still not moving, barely blinking as she stares ahead into nothingness, as if she's completely and utterly lost.

'Who is this?' someone asks on the other end of the line.

'Luke . . . Price.'

'Oh . . .' He sounds wary. 'This is Detective Stephner. Is Violet there with you?'

'She is but she can't talk right now,' I tell him, smoothing my hand over her head, which seems to be helping, her breathing settling just a little bit, but her eyes are still so hollow. 'What exactly did you say to her?'

'I'm not at liberty to tell you that.' He pauses. 'Are you guys back in Laramie yet?'

I glance at the road in front of us. 'No, we're headed back now and are about halfway there . . . why?'

'Well, I would suggest turning around and taking Violet with you to stay somewhere just for a few days,' he says. 'Just until we can get some answers about someone.'

I continue to run my fingers up and down Violet's cheek and she nuzzles into my touch. 'Does this have anything to do with my mother?' I ask quietly.

'You need to speak to Violet. That's all I'm going to say,' he replies in a formal tone. 'Have her call me as soon as she calms down.'

'Okay,' I say, then we hang up and I put the phone on the dashboard and stare down at her; her head on my lap, her eyes so full of fear. 'Baby do you want to talk about it?' I ask, fighting to keep my voice calm. I don't want to push her, but I'm desperate to know if this has anything to do with my mother.

She shakes her head and closes her eyes as my fingers brush through her hair. 'No, not yet.'

My hand pauses in her hair. 'The detective . . . he said it'd be better if you maybe stayed away from Laramie for a bit.'

'Okay, you can leave me on the side of the road.' She's not joking either. In fact, she sounds hopeful that I'll do it.

I'm not sure how long I stay parked on the side of the freeway, trying to figure out what to do—where to take her. Back to Vegas? I don't want to do that, don't want to go back to that kind of environment. There's only one other choice, one for which I have to swallow up what little pride I have left, before I take out the phone and dial Dad's number. He answers after two rings and I sputter it out before I back out.

'Hey, I need another favor.'

Epilogue

One day later . . .

Luke

My dad lives in this section of town in San Diego where the streets are sloped and lined with tall, slender town homes and trees. The air smells like the ocean and by the time we arrive there it's veering toward the next night, the sun setting, the sky painted orange and pink.

Violet barely spoke the entire drive and only moved when she got out to go to the bathroom. I took the opportunity to call Kayden and get Coach's number so I could talk to him about missing the first week of practice.

'You know he's weird about that shit,' Kayden said, reminding me just how much I might be screwing up my perfect schedule that I'd worked so hard to maintain.

'I know,' I replied. 'But it is what it is . . . I can't make it there.'

'Can I ask why?'

'Remember when you beat the shit out of Caleb and you told me something along the lines of you were doing it because someone hurt Callie so badly? And you did it without a second thought, even if it meant your own life was going to get screwed up?'

'Yeah . . .' He was confused and a little uncomfortable, mainly because we don't talk about this stuff.

'Well, I'm not beating anyone up or anything, but someone needs me right now and I really don't give a shit about football or school at the moment,' I said. 'Only her.'

He paused. 'Is it Violet?'

'Yeah.'

Another pause and then he said, 'Tell Coach it's a family emergency. I did that once and even though he was pissed, he let me off the hook.'

'Thanks man,' I said, then quickly had to hang up because Violet had returned from the bathroom and I didn't want her to hear what I was doing and try to convince me otherwise.

'I bought some skittles,' she said as she returned to the truck, and that was the last thing she said for the next five hours, eventually falling asleep and not even waking up when we arrived at my dad's house—I had to carry her inside.

'I'm worried about her,' I tell my dad as I go back into the kitchen, after I've carried Violet to the guest bedroom and laid her in the bed. I don't want to leave her alone too long. I'm worried she'll do something reckless, like she tried to do back at my uncle's, with the window incident.

I'm standing in the kitchen with my dad, tired and in desperate need of some sleep and food. I called Seth on the drive here and asked him if my dad could wire some money to his account and then if he could withdraw it and leave it in Geraldson's mailbox as per the agreement I'd made with Geraldson a few minutes earlier.

'Yeah, sure. Whatever will help,' he'd replied, and then being him had of course pressed for more details, which I promised him I'd do later if he did the favor.

It was sort of strange that I asked Seth for help. A year or so ago I would have asked Kayden to do it, but I guess things change. Seth knows some of the shit that goes on in my life too—not all but some.

'How long has she been like that?' my dad asks, sitting down on one of the barstools with a mug of coffee in front of him. It's so strange seeing him in person. He looks different from what I remember: older, thinning brown hair, more wrinkles, thicker in the waist, but healthier—a stranger who I know and yet feel uncomfortable around. Thankfully it's late enough that Trevor is in bed. I haven't had any time to prepare myself to meet my dad, let alone his husband.

'Since she talked to the detective on the phone,' I say, sitting on a barstool beside him, my eyelids so heavy I can barely keep them open. I drove straight here, barely making stops except to put gas in the truck and I'm ready to crash, sleep off the last day.

'Did it . . . Was it . . .' He struggles. 'Was it about Mira?'

'I don't know,' I tell him with a shrug. 'She won't talk about it, whatever it is. But the detective I talked to briefly said it might be best if I took her somewhere away from Laramie for a while.' I lower my head onto the countertop, the coldness of the surface feeling good against my warm skin. 'Jesus, I have no idea what to do. She's scaring me . . .'

My father puts his hand on my back and I jump, but don't shove it off. 'Go get some rest and then I'll help you talk to her in the morning. I'll help you, Luke . . . I'm here for you . . .'

There are a million things I want to say at that moment, some rude and some nice, but all I say is, 'Thanks.' Because I'm tired.

Then I push out of the chair and go up to the guest room, ready to collapse in the bed. But instead I find Violet standing by the window, staring out at the street with her arms folded across her chest. I let out a nervous breath and cross the room to her, hesitating before I wrap my arms around her.

She doesn't fight me, doing the opposite and leaning against me, as if I'm the only thing that's holding her up. 'They found evidence that might help the arrest with your mom,' she says quietly. 'But they have to find her first.'

'Wait a minute? Find her?' I slant to the side to look her in the eyes. 'She's not at the house?'

She shakes her head, refusing to make eye contact with me. 'And the landlord and neighbors said she hasn't been for a while.'

My arms tighten around her, worried that she's suddenly going to push away and run, like she did a couple of months ago. 'We'll find her,' I promise. 'No matter what it takes.' I kiss the back of her head and she nuzzles into me. 'I'll make sure of it.'

'There's more.' Her voice sounds so hollow, the

moonlight reflecting the pain in her eyes, so overwhelming, almost as if the pain possesses her. It's a look that'll haunt me forever. 'It's about Preston and my parents . . . well, my mother anyway.'

'Okay.' I have no idea where this is going, but I prepare myself for something extremely bad, because of how she reacted in the car and the look on her face right now.

'Apparently that's not even Preston's real name . . . and he had all these pictures of me and my family in this little room under the house that I'd always thought he kept drugs in . . . and he might have been my mother's drug dealer back when she was doing drugs . . . something I didn't know until now . . .' A tear slips from her eye and she doesn't bother wiping it away. 'Which not only means that my mother wasn't who I've been thinking she was my entire life, but that Preston might have had something to do with their deaths . . . the detective said it's not for sure . . . But fuck . . . what if it is . . . what if he had something to do with it . . .?' Another tear and then another. 'All that time I spent with him . . . those things I did . . . God, I think I'm going to be sick.' That's when she starts to cry, tears pouring out of her eyes as her legs give out on her.

Tears burn at my own eyes. Jesus, life is so unfair. So cruel. To put one person through this much. Holding her weight for her, I scoop her up in my arms and carry her to the bed. I can't even think of anything to say because there are no words that exist for moments like these. Honestly, I can't even believe it's possible. How can one girl's world be so shattered? So broken. So painful. I want to take all of it for her—I would in a heartbeat if I could. But instead I have to lie here with her in my arms and listen to her break apart. And eventually, my own eyes start to water.

'How can they be sure?' I ask, fighting to keep balance in my voice. 'The police, I mean. They're going to find out if he had anything to do with it or not, right?'

'Yeah.' She buries her face in my chest. 'What if he is . . . what if I let him touch me the way that he did and that whole time he took their lives . . .?' Her hands find the bottom of my shirt and she grips tightly. 'I can't deal with any more of this . . .' She sucks in a breath, then another. 'Pain. I'm so sick of having no one . . . of having every relationship ruined.'

My arms tighten around her and I hold her with every part of me. 'No matter what happens, I'm going to be here for you.'

She presses her face closer to my chest, balling herself

up against me as she continues to cry. 'Promise me you'll never leave me.' It's hard to hear her through the crying, but the soft utter of the words is enough that a few tears escape my eyes. I want to wipe them away so she can't see me falling apart, but I don't want to let her go either.

'Never,' I promise and I mean it more than I've ever meant anything. 'No matter what happens, I'll always be here for you.'

I want to tell her right here that I love her, but I know it's in no way the right time. So instead I try to show her, holding her and letting her cry, vowing to myself that I'll try and find a way to take some of her pain away, no matter what it takes.

Have you read the first book in the story of
Violet and Luke?

Find out how it all began in

The Destiny of Violet & Luke

Read on for an extract . . .

Prologue

Luke

(Eight years old)

I hate running, but it always seems like I'm doing it. Always running everywhere. Always trying to hide. I hide just as much as I run, but if I don't then bad things will happen. Like getting found. Or getting forced to do things that make me sick to my stomach. Getting forced to help *her*.

"Come out, come out wherever you are," my mom sing-songs as I run out the front door of my house. Her voice is slurred, which means she's been taking her medication again. She takes her medication a lot and it doesn't make any sense to me. I have to take medication sometimes, too, but because I get sick. Whenever she takes it, it seems to make her sicker.

She used to not be like this, well not as bad anyway. About a year ago, when my dad was still around she would act normal and not take medication. Now, though, she does it a lot and I think she might be going crazy. At least she seems that way compared to everyone else's moms. I see them picking up my friends from school and they always look happy and put together. My friends are always glad to see them and they don't run and hide from them, like I do all the time.

I race around to the back of the house, running away from the sound of her voice as she chases after me, looking for me. She's always looking for me and I hate when she does—hate her sometimes for always making me run and hide. And for finding me. I usually hide underneath the bed or in the closet or somewhere else in the house, but she's been finding me quicker lately, so today I decided to hide outside.

As I make it to the back porch stairs, I slam to a stop, panting to catch my breath. There's just enough room for me to duck down below the decaying boards and hide underneath. I pull my legs up against me and lower my head onto my knees. The sunlight sparkles through the cracks in the wood and down on me. I'm nervous because if the sun can see me, then maybe she might see me, too.

I scoot back, closer to the bottom step and out of the sunlight, and then I hold my breath as I hear the screen door hinges creak.

"Luke," my mom says from up on the top step. She shuffles across the wood in her slippers and the screen door bangs shut. "Luke, are you out here?"

I tuck my face into my arms, sucking back the tears, even though I want to cry—she'll hear me if I do. Then she'll probably want to hug me better and I don't like when she does that.

I don't like a lot of things she does and how wrong she makes my life feel.

"Luke Price," she warns, stepping down the stairs. I peek up at her through the cracks and see her pink furry slippers. The smoke from her cigarette makes my stomach burn. "If you're out here and you're ignoring me, you're going to be in trouble." She almost sings it, like it's a song to some game we're playing. Sometimes I think that's what this is to her. A game that I always lose.

The stairs creak as she slowly walks down to the bottom step. Ashes from her cigarette scatter across the ground and all over my head. A few land in my mouth, but I don't spit. I stay as still as I can, fighting to keep my heart from beating so loudly as my palms sweat.

Finally, after what seems like forever, she turns around and heads up the stairs back to the house. "Fine, have it your way, then," she says.

It's never my way and I know better than to think so. That's why I stay still even after the screen door shuts. I barely breathe as the wind blows and the sunlight dims. I wait until the sky is almost gray before I peek up through the cracks in the stairs. If I had my way I'd stay here forever, hiding under the stairs, but I'm hungry and tired.

I can't see or hear her anymore so I lean forward, poke my head out from under the stairs. The coast looks clear so I put my hands down on the dirt and crawl out onto the grass. I get to my feet and brush the dirt and the rocks off my torn jeans. Then, taking a deep breath, I run around to the side of the house and hurry quickly up the fence line until I make it to the front yard.

I've never liked where we live that much. Everyone's grass always looks yellow and all the houses look like they need to be repainted. My mom says it's because we're poor and this is all we can afford thanks to my dad leaving us and that he doesn't care and that's why he never comes to see me. I'm not sure I believe her since my mom's always telling lies. Like how she promises me time and time again that this will be the last time she makes me do things I don't want to do.

I stand in the front yard for a while, figuring out where to go. I could climb through my sister's bedroom window and hide out there until she gets home, then maybe she can help me. But she's been acting strange lately and gets annoyed whenever I talk to her. She's lucky because Mom never seems to notice her as much as she notices me. I don't know why. I do my best to blend in. I don't make messes, keeping the house clean and organized like she likes it. I keep quiet. I stay in my room a lot and organize my toys in categories, just the way she likes them, yet she's always calling for me. But Amy seems invisible to her.

She's so lucky. I wish I were invisible.

I decide to go for a walk down to the gas station at the corner where I can get a candy bar or something because my stomach hurts from hunger. But as my feet touch the sidewalk, I hear the front door swing open.

"Luke, get in here right now," she says in a frenzy, snapping her fingers and pointing to the ground below her feet. "I need you."

I freeze, wishing I were brave enough to take off running down the sidewalk. Just leave. Never come back. Sleep in a box because a box seems so much nicer than my sterilized house. But I'm not brave and I turn around and face her just like she wants me to. She's holding the door open, her hair pulled up messily on top of her head and she's wearing this purple tank top and plaid shorts that she always wears. It's pretty much like a uniform for her, except she doesn't have a job. Not a good one anyway where she has to wear a uniform. Instead, she sells her medicine to creepy men who are always staring at her or Amy when she walks out of her bedroom.

She crooks her finger at me. "Get in here."

An unsteady breath leaves my mouth as I trudge to the front door, a nauseating feeling rising in my stomach. It happens every time she needs me. I get sick to my stomach at the thoughts of what she's going to make me do creep inside my head.

When I reach the stairs, she moves back, not looking happy, but not looking sad either. She holds the door open for me, watching me with her brown eyes that remind me of the bag of marbles she made me throw away because they didn't look right. Once I'm inside, she closes the door and shoves the deadbolt over. She fastens the small chain and then clicks the lock on the doorknob before turning around.

The curtains are shut and there's a lit cigarette on a teal glass ashtray that's on the coffee table, filling the room with smoke. There's a sofa just behind the table and it's covered in plastic to keep "the dirty air from ruining the fabric," my mother told me once. She always thinks the dirt in the air is going to do something to either the house or her, which is why she rarely goes outside anymore.

"Why'd you run off?" she asks me as she walks over the sofas and flops down in it. She picks up her cigarette and ashes it, before putting it into her mouth. She takes a deep inhale and seconds later a cloud of smoke circles around her sore-covered face. "Were you playing a game or something?"

I nod, because telling her I was playing a game is much better than telling her I was hiding from her. "Yes."

She takes another drag from the cigarette and then stares at the row of cat figurines on one of the shelves lining the living room walls. Each row on the shelf is organized with figurines, according to breed. She did it once when she was having one of her episodes from too much medication, the one that makes her stay awake for a long, long time, not the stuff that makes her pass out. The glass clinking together and her incoherent murmuring had woken me up when she was rearranging the figurines and when I'd walked out she was moving like crazy, frantically trying to get the animals into order or "something bad was going to happen." She knew it was—she could feel it in her bones. I think something bad already did happen, though. A lot of bad things actually.

"Luke, pay attention," my mom says. I tear my gaze away from the figurines, wishing I was one of them, so I could be up on the shelf, watching what's about to happen instead of taking part in it. She switches her cigarette to her other hand and then leans to the side, grabbing her small wooden "medication box." She sets it on her lap, puts the cigarette into her mouth one last time, and then places it down so she can turn on the lamp. "Now quit messing around and come here, would ya?"

My body gets really tight and I glance over my shoulder at the front door, crossing my fingers that Amy will come home and interrupt us long enough that I can find another place to hide. But she doesn't and I'm stuck out here. With her.

"Do I have to?" I utter quietly.

She nods with chaotic frenzy in her eyes. "You need to."

Shaking, I turn back around and trudge over to the sofa. I take a seat beside her and she pats me on the head several times like I'm her pet. She does that a lot and it makes me wonder how she sees me; if I'm kind of like a pet to her instead of her kid.

"You were a bad boy today," she says as her fingers continue to touch my hair. I hate it when she does that and it makes me want to shave my head bald so she won't be able to touch me. "You should have come when I called you."

"I'm sorry," I lie, because I'm only sorry I was found. I need to find better hiding spots and stay in them long enough that she'll stop looking for me, then maybe I can become invisible like Amy.

"It's okay." She strokes my cheek and then my neck before pulling her hand away. She places a kiss on my cheek and I shut my eyes, holding my breath, trapping in a scream because I want to shout: *Don't touch me!* "I know deep down you're a good boy."

No, I'm not. I'm terrible because I hate you. I really do. I hate you so much I wish you were gone.

She starts humming a song she made up as she removes the lid from the box and carefully sets it aside. I don't even have to look inside it to know what's in it. A spoon, a lighter, a small plastic baggie that holds this stuff that looks almost like brown sugar, a thin piece of cotton, a half a bottle of water, a big rubber band thing, and a needle and syringe that she probably stole from the stash I use to give myself insulin shots.

"Now you remember what to do?" she asks, and then starts humming again.

I nod, tears burning in the corners of my eyes because I don't want to do it—I don't want to do anything that she tells me. "Yes."

"Good." She pats my head again, this time a little rougher.

I don't watch her as she opens the baggie and puts some of the brown sugary stuff onto the metal spoon along with some water, but I can pretty much visualize her movements since I've seen her do this a lot, sometimes twice a day. It really depends on how much she's talking to herself. If it's a lot then she brings out the needle a lot. But sometimes, when she gets quieter, it's not so bad. I like the quieter days, ones where she's either focused on cleaning or stuck in her head. Or I'll even take her being passed out.

She heats the spoon with the lighter as she mutters lyrics under her breath. She actually has a beautiful voice, but the words she sings are frightening. After the spoon is heated enough, she ties the rubber band around her arm, I sit on the couch beside her, tapping my fingers on my leg, pretending I'm in there instead of here. Anywhere but here.

I hate her.

"All right, Luke, help me out, okay," she finally says after she's melted her medication into a pool of liquid and sucked some into the syringe.

I turn toward her, shaking nervously. Always shaking. Always nervous, all the time. Always so worried I'll do something wrong. Mess up. She instantly hands me the syringe and then extends her arm onto my lap. She has these purple marks and red dots all over her upper forearm from all the other times the needles have gone into her. Her veins are really dark on her skin and I don't like the sight of the needle going in just as much as she does like it. Like a routine, I point the needle toward her arm near where all the other dots on her skin are.

My hand quivers unsteadily. "Please don't make me do this," I whisper. "Please Mom." I don't know why I even try, though. She'll do anything to get her medication. And I mean anything. Dark things that normal people wouldn't do.

"Deep breaths, remember?" She ignores me as she wraps her free arm around the back of my neck. "Remember, don't miss the vein. You can mess up my arm or even kill me if you're not careful, okay?" She says it so sweetly like it's a nice thing to say and will make me less nervous.

But it makes things worse, especially because part of me wishes I'd miss the vein. I have to take a lot of breaths before I can settle down inside and get my thoughts from going to that dark place they always want to go, reminding myself that I don't want to hurt her. *I don't.*

When I get my nerves under control the best that I can, I sink the needle into her vein, like I've done hundreds of times. Each time it gets to me, like I'm sticking the needle in my own skin and feeling the sting. I wince as her muscles tense a little underneath the poke of the needle. As I push in the plunger, the medicine enters her veins and seconds later she lets out this weird noise, before sinking back on the couch, pulling me down with her. I hurry and pull the needle out before we fall down completely onto the couch cushions.

"Thank you, Luke," she says sleepily, patting my head with her hand as she holds me against her. Her throat makes this vibrating noise, like she's trying to hum again, but the noise is trapped like I am.

I press my lips together, staring at the wall across the room, barely breathing. After a while, her arm falls lifelessly to the side, her hand hitting the floor as her eyelids flutter shut and I'm temporarily freed from her hold.

I sit up, sucking the tears back, hating her for making me do this and hating myself for doing it and being secretly glad she's passed out. I toss the syringe down on the table, then I push to my feet. Using all my strength, I rotate her to her side because sometimes she throws up. I have a house full of quiet now, just how I like it. Yet, at the same time I don't like it because the emptiness gets to me. What I really want is what all the other kids have. The ones I see at the park playing on swings while their parents push them higher. They're always laughing and smiling. Everyone always seems to be, except for me. Every time I get close I always remember this feeling I have inside me right now, this vile, icky feeling, mixed with hatred and sadness that makes me sick all the time. It always wipes the smile right off my face and I don't even bother trying anymore. Happiness isn't real. It's make-believe.

I throw the syringe and spoon into the box, wondering if my life will always be this way. If I'll always carry so much sadness and hate inside me. I'm shaking by the time I get everything into the box and I feel like I need to flee somewhere—run again. I can't take this anymore. I can't take living here. With her.

"I can't take it!" I shout at the top of my lungs and ram my fist into the coffee table. My hand makes this popping sound and it hurts so bad tears sting at my eyes. I cry out in pain, sinking to the floor, but of course no one hears me.

No one ever does.

Violet

(Thirteen years old)

I hate moving. Not just from house to house, but from family to family. I hate moving my legs and arms, moving forward in my life, because it usually means I'm going to someplace new. If I had my way, I'd remain motionless, never moving forward, never going anywhere. The thing is I always have to, it's not a choice, and I never know exactly where I'm going or who I'll be stuck with. Sometimes the families are fine, but sometimes not. Drunks. Religious freaks. Haters. Wandering hands.

The family I'm staying with now always tells me everything I do is wrong and that I should be more like their daughter, Jennifer. I'm not sure why they took me in to begin with. They seem pretty content with the child they have and I'm just a decoration, a flashy object they can show off to their friends so they can get told how great they are for taking in such a messed-up child. I'm the unwanted orphan they took in, hoping to fix me and make their family appear wonderful.

"It was so nice of you to give her a home," a woman with fiery red hair tells Amelia, who's my mother at the moment. She's having one of her neighborhood shindigs, which she does a lot, then complains about them later to her husband. "These poor children really do need a roof over their head."

Amelia glances at me, sitting in a chair at the table where I was directed to stay the entire party. "Yes, but it's hard, you know." She's wearing this yellow sweater that reminds me of a canary that was a pet at one of my foster parent's homes that never stopped chattering. She arranges some crackers and sliced cheese onto a large flowery platter and then heads for the refrigerator. "She's kind of a problem child." She opens the fridge door and takes out a large pitcher of lemonade. She looks over at me again, then leans toward the redhead, lowering her voice. "She's so angry all the time and she broke this vase the other day because she couldn't find her shoes...but we're working on fixing her."

Angry all the time. That's what everyone seems to say; I'm so angry at the world and it's understandable considering what I've been through, yet no one wants to deal with it. That I probably have too much rage inside me. That I'm broken. Unstable. Maybe even dangerous. All the things that no adult wants in a child. They want smiles and laughter, children who will make them smile and laugh, too. I'm the dark, morbid side of childhood. I swear they're waiting around for me to do something that will give them an excuse to get rid of me and they can tell everyone they tried but I was just too messed up to be fixed.

"And her nightmares," Amelia continues. "She wakes up screaming every night and she wet the bed the other night. She even came running into our room, saying she was scared to sleep alone." Her eyes glide to the tattered purple teddy bear I'm hugging. "She's very immature and carries that stuffed animal around with her everywhere... it's strange."

I hate her. She doesn't understand what it's like to see things that most people can't even admit exist. The ugly truth, painted in red, stuck in my head, images I can't shake. Death. Cruelty. Terror. People taking other peoples' lives as if lives mean nothing. Then they leave me behind to carry the foul, rotting truth with me. Alone. *Why did they leave me behind?*

This teddy bear is all I have left of a time when ugly didn't consume my life.

I turn my head away from the sound of her voice and stare out the window at the sunlight reflecting against a lawn ornament shaped like a tulip, and hug the teddy bear against my chest, the one my dad gave me as an early birthday present the day before he died. There are little red, heart-shaped beads on the tulip and when they catch in the light they flicker and make dots dance against the concrete on the back porch. It's pretty to watch and I focus on them, shoving my anger down and bottling it up—trying to stay in control of my emotions. Otherwise all the feelings I've buried will escape and I'll have no choice but to find a way to shut it down—find my adrenaline rush.

Besides, Amelia doesn't need to repeat what I already know. I know what I do every night, just like I know what I am to them, just like I know in a few months or so they'll get tired of me and send me to another place with a different home where everything I do will annoy those people, too, and eventually they'll pass me along. It's like clockwork and I don't expect anything more. Expecting only leads to disappointment. I expected things once when I was little—that I'd continue to grow up with my mom and dad, smile, and be happy—but that dream was crushed the day they died.

"Violet," Amelia snaps and I quickly turn my head to her. She and her redheaded friend are staring at me with worry and a hint of fear in their eyes and I wonder just how much her friend knows about me. Does she know about that night? What I saw? What I escaped? What I didn't escape? Does it make her afraid of me? "Are you listening to me?" she asks.

I shake my head. "No."

She crooks her eyebrow at me as she opens the cupboard above her head. "No, what?"

I set the teddy bear on my lap and tell myself to shut off the anger because the last time I released it, I ended up breaking lots of things, then got sent here. "No, ma'am."

Her eyebrow lowers as she selects a few cans of beans out from a top cupboard. "Good, now if you would just listen the first time then we'd be on track."

"I'm listening now," I say to her, which results in her face pinching. "Sorry. I'm listening now, ma'am."

She glares at me coldly as she stacks the cans on the countertop and takes a can opener out from a drawer. "I said would you go into the garage and get me some hamburger meat from the storage freezer."

I nod and hop off the chair, taking the teddy bear with me, relieved to get out of the stuffy kitchen and away from her friend who keeps looking at me like I'm about to stab her. As I head out the door into the garage I hear Amelia saying, "I think we might contact social services to take her back... she just wasn't what we were expecting."

Never expect anything, I want to turn around and tell her, but I continue out into the garage. The lights are on and I trot down the steps and wind around the midsize car toward the freezer in the corner. But I pause when I notice Jennifer in the corner, along with a boy and two girls who are messing around with bikes in the garage.

"Well, well look what the dog dragged in," she sneers as she moves her bike away from the wall. Her bike is pink, just like the dress she's wearing. I used to have a bike once, too, only it was purple, because I hate pink. But I never learned how to ride it and now it's part of my old life, boxed away and sold along with the rest of my childhood. "It's Violet and that stupid bear." She glances at her friends. "She always carries it around with her like a little baby or something."

I keep the bear close and disregard her the best that I can, because it's all I can do. This isn't my house or my family and no one's going to take my side. I'm alone in the world. It's something I learned early on and becoming used to the idea of always being alone has made life a little easier to live over the last several years.

I hurry past her and her friends who laugh when she utters under her breath that I smell like a homeless person. I open the freezer and take out a frozen pound of hamburger meat, then shut the lid and turn back for the door. Jennifer has abandoned her bike to strategically place herself in front of my path back to the door.

"Would you please move?" I ask politely, tucking the hamburger meat under one of my arms and my teddy bear under the other. I dodge to the side, but Jennifer sidesteps with me, her hands out to the side.

"Troll," the boy laughs and it's echoed by the cackling of laughter.

"This is my house," Jennifer says with a smirk. "Not yours, so you don't get to tell me what to do."

I hold up the hamburger meat, fighting to keep my temper under control. "Yeah, but your mom asked me to get this for her."

She puts her hands on her hips and says to me with an attitude, "That's because she thinks of you as our maid. In fact, I overheard her talking to my dad the other day, telling him that's why they're fostering you—because they needed someone to clean up the house."

Don't let her get to you. It doesn't matter. Nothing does. "Get out of my way," I say through gritted teeth.

She shakes her head. "No way. I don't have to listen to you, you loser, smelly, crazy girl."

The other kids laugh and it takes a lot of energy not to clock her in the face. *You were taught to be better than that. Mom and Dad would want me to be better.* I move around to the other side but she matches my step and kicks me in the shin. A throbbing pain ricochets up my leg, but I don't give her the satisfaction of a reaction, remaining calm.

"No wonder you don't have any parents. They probably didn't want you," she snickers. "Oh wait, that's right. They died...you probably even killed them yourself."

"Shut up," I warn, shaking as I step closer to her. I can feel anger blazing inside me, on the brink of exploding.

"Or what?" she says, refusing to back off. The boy on the floor stands up and starts to head toward us with a look on his face that makes me want to bolt. But I won't. I'm sure they'll chase me if I do and in the end I'm going to get blamed for this incident.

"What do you mean, she killed her parents?" he asks, wiping some grime off his forehead with his thumb.

Jennifer grins maliciously and then turns to him. "Haven't you heard the story about her?"

"Shut up." I cut her off as I move so close to her I almost knock her over, then raise my hand up in front of me, like I'm going to shove her. "I'm warning you."

She keeps talking as if I don't exist. "Her parents were murdered." She glances at me with hate and cruelty in her eyes. "I heard my mom saying she was the one who found them, but I'm guessing it's because she did it herself because she's *crazy*."

I see the image of my mom and dad in their bedroom surrounded by blood and I lose it. I quickly shove the image out of my head until all I see is red. Red everywhere. Blood. Red. Blood. Death. And a stupid little girl who won't walk away from it.

I throw the hamburger meat down on the ground, not concerned about what happens to me, and grab a handful of her long blond hair and yank on it. "Take it back!" I shout, pulling harder as I circle around to the front of the car, away from the boy, dragging Jennifer with me.

She starts to cry, her head tipped back, tears spilling out of her eyes. "You evil bitch!"

"Let her go!" the boy yells, running around the car at us. "You crazy psycho." He turns to the other girls and tells them to go get someone and then they take off running, looking at me like I'm crazy, too.

I know it'll be just moments before Amelia comes out and then not too long after she'll call social services to come take me away. I'm trembling with anger and hate all directed toward Jennifer, because she's the one here in front of me. No one else. My vision blurs along with my head and my heart and it feels like I'm back at my childhood home walking into the room again, seeing the blood... hearing the voices...

I'm trembling so much my fingers have no strength left to hold on to Jennifer and I release her. She immediately stumbles forward into the front of the car. Regaining her balance, she spins around and shoves me so hard I fall to the ground and my head bangs against the wall.

"You psycho!" she shouts, her face bright red, tears streaming out of her eyes. "My mom and dad are so going to send you away."

I stare at the space on the floor in front of her feet, hugging my teddy bear, motionless.

She lets out a frustrated grunt and then stomps her foot on the floor before running out of the garage.

Moments later, Amelia comes rushing in, shouting before she even reaches me. "You're done here! Do you understand?"

"Yes." I don't have a single drop of emotion left and my voice sounds hollow.

"Yes, what?" She waits for me to answer her with her arms crossed.

I don't reply because I don't have to anymore. I'm finished with this home. There's no erasing what just happened. I can't change the past just as much as I can't control my future.

She gets livid, her face tinting pink as she tries to contain her fury. She tells me I'm worthless. She tells me that no one will want me. She tells me I'm leaving. She tells me everything I already know.

"Are you even listening to me?!" she shouts and I shake my head. Fuming, she snatches the bear from my hands.

That snaps me out of my motionless trance. "Hey, that's mine!" I cry, jumping to my feet and lunging for the bear. My shoulder bumps into her arm as she moves it out of my reach.

She moves back and tucks her arm behind her back. "Consider it a punishment for hurting my daughter."

"Your daughter deserved it." I panic. If she does anything to that bear I won't be able to take it. I need that bear or else I can't survive—don't want to. *Why did I survive?*

"Well, when you're ready to apologize to Jennifer, you can have it back." She heads toward the door to the house where Jennifer is standing with a smile on her face, expecting an apology.

"Sorry," I practically growl, wanting the damn bear back enough that I'll do whatever she asks at the moment. "Please, don't take it away." Desperation burns in my voice. "It's all I have left of my mom and dad—it's all I have of them." I'm begging, weak, pathetic. I hate it. I hate myself. But I need that bear.

Jennifer grins at me as she crosses her arms and leans against the doorway, her cheeks stained red from the drying tears. "Mom, I don't think she's really sorry."

Amelia studies me for a moment. "I don't think she is either." She frowns disappointedly, like she's finally seeing that she can't fix me, then turns for the door with my bear in her hand. "You can have it back when I see a real apology come out of that mouth of yours. And you better make it quick because you won't be here for very much longer."

"I said I was sorry," I yell out with my hands balled into fists at my side. "What the hell else do you want me to say?"

She doesn't answer me and goes into the house with my bear. Jennifer smirks at me before turning for the house, shutting the lights off and then closing the door on her way inside.

I'm suffocated by the dark. But it's nothing I can't handle. Seeing things is much harder than seeing nothing but the dark. I like the dark.

I slide down to the ground and lean back against the wall, hugging my knees to my chest as I let the darkness settle over me. A few tears slip out and drip down my cheeks and I let more stream out, telling myself it's okay, because I'm in the dark, and nothing can be seen in the dark.

But after a while I can't get the tears to stop as what

Jennifer and the other kids said plays on repeat inside my head. I think about the last time I saw my parents lying in their coffins and how they got there. The blood. I'll never forget the blood. On the floor. On me.

More tears spill out and soon my whole face is drenched with them. My heart thrashes against my chest and I tug at my hair as I scream through clenched teeth, kicking my feet against the floor. Invisible razors and needles stab underneath my skin. I can't turn off the emotions. I can't think straight. My lungs need air. I hurt. I ache. I can't take it anymore. I need it out. I need to breathe.

I stumble to my feet and through the dark, until I find the door that leads to the driveway. I shove the door open, sprint outside into the sunlight and race past the cars parked in the driveway and toward the curb. I don't slow down until I'm approaching the highway in front of the house where cars zip up and down the road. With no hesitation, I walk into the middle of the road and stand on the yellow dotted line with my arms held out to the side. Tears pool in my eyes as I blink against the sunlight, my pulse speeding up the longer I stay there and that rush of energy that has become the only familiar thing in my life takes over.

It feels like I'm flying, head-on into something other than being moved around, passed around, given away, tossed aside, forgotten. I have the unknown in front of me and I have no idea what's going to happen. It feels so liberating. So I stay in place, even when I hear the roar of a car's engine. I wait until

I hear the sound of the tires. Until I see the car. Until it's close enough that the driver honks their horn. Until I feel the swish of an adrenaline rush, drenching the sadness and panic out of my body and mind. Until my emotions subside and all I feel is exhilaration. Then I jump to the right where the road meets the grass as the car makes a swerve to the left to go around me. Brakes screech. A horn honks. Someone shouts.

I lie soundless in the grass, feeling twenty times better than I did in the garage. I feel content in a dark hole of numbness; a place where I can feel okay being the child that no one wants. The child that probably would have been better off dying with her parents, instead of being left alive and alone.

Have you read Jessica's bestselling Ella & Micha series?

Begin with the first book,

The Secret of Ella and Micha

and prepare to lose yourself in one of the most intense, passionate love stories you will ever read.

The girl he thinks he loves needs to disappear.
I don't want tonight to be irreversible, so I pull away, breathing him in one last time.

Ella and Micha have been best friends since childhood, until one tragic night shatters their relationship and Ella decides to leave everything behind to start a new life at college, including Micha.

But now it's summer break and she has nowhere else to go but home. Ella fears everything she worked so hard to bury might resurface, especially with Micha living right next door. Micha is sexy, smart, confident, and can get under Ella's skin like no one else can. He knows everything about her, including her darkest secrets. And he's determined to win back the girl he lost, no matter what it takes.

Out now.

Don't miss Jessica's latest, passionate series.

Begin with the first book,

Breaking Nova

Nova Reed used to have dreams of becoming a famous drummer, of marrying her true love. But all of that was taken away in an instant. Now she's getting by as best she can, though sometimes that means doing things the old Nova would never do. Things that are slowly eating away at her spirit. Every day blends into the next, until she meets Quinton Carter.

Quinton once got a second chance at life, but he doesn't want it. The tattoos on his chest are a constant reminder of what he's done, what he's lost. He's sworn never to allow happiness into his life, but then beautiful, sweet Nova makes him smile. He knows he's too damaged to get close to her, yet she's the only one who can make him feel alive again. Quinton will have to decide: does he deserve to start over? Or should he pay for his past forever?

Out now.

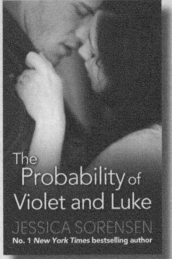